STEAM
DESIGN CHALLENGES

Written by

Michelle Powers, Teri Barenborg,
Tari Sexton, and Lauren Monroe

Editor: Christie Weltz
Designer/Production: Tawney Johnson
Art Director: Moonhee Pak
Project Director: Stacey Faulkner

DEDICATION

This book is dedicated to all of the educators and children who have inspired us to make education a hands-on experience and, most importantly, instilled within us a lifelong love of learning.

ACKNOWLEDGMENTS

First and foremost, we would like to thank our families and friends who have supported us in so many ways—from the steadfast support of our chosen career path and passion all the way through the inspiration and creation of this series of books. Each of us has an amazing support system that has not only encouraged us but also made it possible for us to devote our time to this project. A sincere thank-you to our colleagues, both past and present, as well as all the educators who have inspired us to create a collection of lessons that encourage students to grow and take ownership of their learning. Without the continued support and encouragement of our dear friend Lynn Howard, these books would not have been possible.

Our school district, St. Lucie Public Schools, known for being the first Kids at Hope school district in the state of Florida, motivated us to build a culture of learning where students state daily that "All children are capable of success. No exceptions." This mindset, along with the work of Carol Dweck and her focus on self-efficacy through a growth mindset, has inspired us to develop lessons that encourage problem solving and perseverance, allowing students to learn from their mistakes.

We would like to thank the various teachers who have opened their doors to us and, more importantly, the students in those classrooms who have tested these exciting lessons during their development. These teachers have allowed us to model, motivate, and encourage them to transition from the "Sage on the Stage" to a "Guide on the Side," giving students the opportunity to drive their own learning.

FOREWORD

Science instruction has changed. Many of us can remember the traditional lecture and note giving model of instruction that had been used for years. I was very alone in my middle school earth science classroom and had no support, no textbook, and no curriculum guide. Living day to day with content that was totally unfamiliar to me, I taught the same way to all students and didn't realize that many of them were not engaged or learning. I had to change and allow for more engagement, exploration, and experimentation. It quickly became the way I taught, and students benefited from the problem solving, collaboration, and inquiry-based activities. When I began my science teaching career years ago, I would have appreciated a resource that provided me with a set of classroom lessons that would challenge and motivate my students.

The Next Generation Science Standards are placing a great emphasis on how we "do science" in the classroom. The integration of science, technology, engineering, arts, and math (STEAM) provides multiple opportunities to include problem solving, engineering practices, and literacy while engaging and motivating students in real-world science experiences.

I really like this book. These lessons are perfect for any teacher who may or may not feel comfortable with teaching science. I really like that the lessons are aligned with the 5E Instructional Model (engage, explore, explain, elaborate, and evaluate). Teachers who use the lessons will address the 5E model and challenge their students with the engineering process. The authors are a team of educators who understand how to teach science. Their teaching has evolved from a traditional approach to becoming facilitators of science knowledge. Teri, Lauren, Michelle, and Tari have spent time learning about the changes in science education and how to design effective science classroom environments. As a professional development associate, I spent three years with them as they explored how to create a balanced science program focused on the Next Generation Science Standards. They invested a large amount of time researching what works and implementing those best practices in their classrooms. I have had the opportunity to be in all of their classrooms and see the engagement and excitement as students collaborate on real-world engineering design problems. The teachers continually reinforce the idea that their students ARE scientists and must practice the habits of scientists. A by-product of these teachers' efforts is a book that other teachers can use today in their classrooms to make it exciting to teach and learn about science!

I am honored that Teri, Lauren, Michelle, and Tari asked me to write the foreword for their book. These teachers truly live and breathe quality science teaching and learning. Their passion, dedication, and commitment to effective science instruction make the activities and ideas in this book invaluable to anyone who wants to get excited about STEAM in their classroom.

Lynn F. Howard
Author and Professional Development Associate
Five Easy Steps to a Balanced Science Program

TABLE OF CONTENTS

GETTING STARTED

LIFE SCIENCE

EARTH AND SPACE SCIENCE

PHYSICAL SCIENCE

ENGINEERING DESIGN

APPENDIX

INTRODUCTION

Science, technology, engineering, art, and math work together to make learning fun!

The Next Generation Science Standards place a greater emphasis on science, technology, engineering, arts, and math (STEAM) in today's classrooms. Schools are implementing and encouraging strong STEAM programs in classrooms in order to provide critical thinking lessons that meet the content standards. STEAM lessons should include problem-solving skills, enhance learning across various disciplines, promote student inquiry, and engage students with real-world situations. Students should be exposed to careers in the STEAM fields and develop skills such as communication, data analysis, following a process, designing a product, and argumentation based on evidence, all while cementing effective collaboration techniques that are necessary for a successful career in STEAM fields.

The lessons in this book are intended to support teachers in implementing the engineering design process in their classroom while integrating national standards from other disciplines. In the engineering design process, teachers become a facilitator rather than the instructional focus. Teachers encourage and guide students to work as a team to find a creative solution without providing step-by-step instructions. The engineering design process shifts away from the long-standing process of the scientific method by placing more emphasis on inquiry. Students are inspired to act as scientists and engineers through the use of sketches, diagrams, mathematical relationships, and literacy connections. By creating their very own models and products based on background information from their studies, students are immediately engaged through a meaningful, rewarding lesson.

Each lesson begins by presenting students with a design challenge scenario, or hook, in order to immediately excite students with a real-world situation that they are on a mission to solve. Students are then given a dilemma, mission, and blueprint design sheet and are asked to collaborate with team members to create several prototypes. Teams are required to choose one prototype to present to their teacher before gathering materials and constructing the chosen design. After testing out their design, teams take part in a class discussion and modify their ideas for redesign and improvement of their prototype. Finally, teams are asked to create a justification piece in order to sell their new prototype. Suggestions for justification projects are provided for each design challenge and include writing a persuasive letter, creating an advertisement or presentation, recording a video, or any other creative ideas they come up with in response to the challenge.

The engaging STEAM design challenge lessons in this book

- Promote analytical and reflective thinking
- Enhance learning across various disciplines
- Encourage students to collaborate to solve real-world design challenges
- Integrate national standards
- Are classroom tested

HOW TO USE THIS BOOK

STEAM design challenges follow the engineering practices that have become recently known in the education field. Engineering practices teach students to solve a problem by designing, creating, and justifying their design. With this model in mind, teachers shift from a "giver of information" to a "facilitator of knowledge." Instead of leading children to the right conclusion through experimental steps, the teacher allows them to work through the process themselves, often changing their plan to improve their original design.

STEAM design challenges allow art to support and enhance the learning of science and math while the engineering process is followed. Students will often use, or be encouraged to use, technology to facilitate their learning. The teacher's role as facilitator allows him or her to guide student thinking by asking questions instead of giving answers. Each lesson covers cross-curricular standards and supports teacher planning for collaboration with other teachers.

Typically, science is not taught as often in elementary school as English, reading, writing, and math, so assignments have been included within the lessons that will assist in giving students skills and practice in those other key subjects.

Lessons focus on key national science standards that are required for many standardized tests and include core English language arts and math standards. National engineering standards as well as national arts and national technology standards are also included in the lessons.

The 5E Instructional Model emphasizes building new ideas using existing knowledge. The components of this model—*Engage, Explore, Explain, Elaborate,* and *Evaluate*—are also a key design feature in the structure of each design challenge. Each design challenge requires the students to respond using mathematical, written, oral, and theatrical skills that are developmentally appropriate while working through each phase of the 5E model.

PHASES OF THE 5E MODEL

LESSON PLAN FORMAT

ENGAGE
Students make connections between past and present learning and focus their thinking on learning outcomes in the activity.

EXPLORE
Students continue to build on their knowledge of their learning through exploration and manipulation of materials.

EXPLAIN
Students support their understanding of the concepts through verbal or written communication. This is also a time when students may demonstrate new skills and when teachers can introduce new vocabulary.

ELABORATE
Students extend their understanding of concepts by obtaining more information about a topic through new experiences.

EVALUATE
Students assess their understanding of key concepts and skills.

Each lesson centers around the Design Challenge Purpose and has two distinct sections—Setting the Stage and STEAM in Action.

- Setting the Stage provides an overview of the lesson, suggested time frame, the background knowledge needed for the teacher and students as well as the standards, target vocabulary, and materials needed.

- STEAM in Action outlines the step-by-step procedure for implementing the lesson.

LESSON PLAN COMPONENTS

SETTING THE STAGE

Header: This section includes the title, suggested time frame for completing the lesson, and the STEAM acronym, in which the capital letters denote the main disciplines that are highlighted in each particular lesson.

Time: A suggested approximate total time for completing each lesson is provided. Because the amount of time teachers have to teach science varies within different states, districts, schools, and even grade levels, you may need to break up the lesson into smaller segments over the course of several days. Natural breaks occur between design and construction, between construction and testing, and between testing and justification.

You may choose to use the lesson ideas in the Student Development section to deepen prior knowledge or you may have your students use the literacy connections and any reputable websites you are familiar with. The lesson ideas in the Justification section are included as an optional extension of the core lesson. None of the activities before or after the core lesson are included in the time estimates. Refer to the suggested lesson timeline on page 11.

Design Challenge Purpose: This is the statement that sets the stage for the design challenge and outlines student objectives and expectations for what they should learn by completing the design challenge.

Teacher Development: This section provides background information about the science content being addressed in the lesson. Information included assists the teacher in understanding key science concepts. We understand that professional development at the elementary teacher level is often geared toward instructional delivery instead of content, especially in the content area of science. This section is provided to help support teachers who may not be as familiar with science content.

Student Development: This section contains a description of the concepts students will need to understand to complete the design challenge successfully. A link to the STEAM Dreamers website, which has active web links and additional suggested lesson ideas for deepening students' understanding of relevant science concepts, can be found on the inside front cover of this book.

Standards: This section lists specific standards for science, technology, engineering, art, math, and English language arts, along with the science and engineering practices and crosscutting concepts. These standards may apply to the activities in the challenges or in the justifications that follow. Please make sure that you review the standards for each of the lessons. The website for each set of standards is listed on page 13.

Target Vocabulary: This section lists target vocabulary to support and enhance the lesson content and to deepen students' understanding of the terms. These vocabulary terms are related to the academic content that the design challenge focuses on; can be used throughout the design challenge when in group discussion; and are an integral component of the standards covered in the challenge. Reviewing the target vocabulary prior to beginning the design challenge is recommended as students need to apply their knowledge of the science concepts and target vocabulary when solving the challenges. Ultimately, the target vocabulary should be revisited multiple times throughout the lesson.

Materials: This section lists materials and equipment that have been selected for the lessons. All materials are meant to be easy to find, inexpensive to purchase, recycled, or commonly available for free. Substitute with similar items if you have them on hand, or visit www.SteamDreamers.com for substitute suggestions.

Literacy Connections: This section lists books or articles that are meant to be used with students prior to the design challenge in order to strengthen their background knowledge and to enhance the integration of literacy in STEAM. These connections can be used during the daily classroom reading block, during small and/or whole-group instruction.

Current literacy connections for each lesson can be accessed through our website: www.SteamDreamers.com.

⚙ STEAM IN ACTION ⚙

The Dilemma: This section includes a unique real-world dilemma or scenario that hooks the students and gets them excited to solve the problem. The dilemma may include a plausible circumstance or a wild story designed to make them think. When planning the design of their prototype, student should ask themselves questions such as *Who is the client? What do we need to create? What is the purpose of the creation? What is the ultimate goal?* Students should discuss these questions with other members of their team and record their responses in their science notebooks.

Note: This is the Engage portion of the lesson, as outlined in the 5E Instructional Model.

The Mission: This section includes the defined challenge statement. This is ultimately the goal that the students are trying to reach.

Blueprint Design: This section instructs students how to focus their thinking in order to solve the problem. Individual team members design their own plans for prototypes. Students are encouraged to add their artistic touches to their thinking. Team members take turns describing their blueprint to the other members of the team. The team then chooses which member's design it will move forward with. This is where students have the opportunity to discuss and make decisions based on their analysis of the Individual Blueprint Design Sheets. Once they have chosen the preferred design, they will draw it on the Group Blueprint Design Sheet and present it to the teacher for approval. Teachers may need to assist students in the labeling of the design and write a description of how the team plans to construct the prototype. Individual and Group Blueprint Design Sheets are found in the Appendix.

Note: This is the Explore portion of the lesson, as outlined in the 5E Instructional Model.

Engineering Design Process: In this section of the lesson, teams will take their group's selected prototype through the engineering design process to create, test, analyze, and redesign as necessary until they have successfully completed their mission.

- The first step in the process is the Engineering Task in which teams will engineer their prototype.

- Students will then test their prototype based upon the mission statement.

- The analysis of their testing will include data collection and determination of success.

- The Redesign and Retest cycle will continue until the team has successfully completed the mission.

Helpful Tips: In this section you'll find suggestions designed to address common issues that may arise during the design challenges. Some tips are geared toward the steps in the engineering design process, and some are more lesson-specific.

Reflections: This section provides suggestions for reflective questions to ask students to help guide and facilitate their thinking at various stages within the engineering design process. It is recommended that students record these questions and their reflections in a science notebook. See pages 16–19 for more information on using a science notebook.

Note: This is the Explain and Elaborate portion of the lesson, as outlined in the 5E Instructional Model.

Justification: This is the stage of the lesson where students apply what they learned in a meaningful and creative way through different mediums, such as technology and the arts. These justifications can occur in many forms: a formal letter, an advertisement, a poem, a jingle, a skit, or a technology-enhanced presentation.

Note: This is the Evaluate portion of the lesson, as outlined in the 5E Instructional Model.

SUGGESTED LESSON TIMELINE

Lesson Progression:

1. Teacher Development/Student Development/Literacy Connections

2. Dilemma/Mission/Blueprint Design

3. Engineering Task/Test Trial/Analyze/Redesign/Reflection

4. Justification

If the lesson will be spread out over multiple days:

Day 1: Teacher Development/Student Development/Literacy Connections

Day 2: Dilemma/Mission/Blueprint Design

Day 3: Engineering Task/Test Trial

Days 4-6: Analyze/Redesign/Reflection (Can be spread over 3 days)

Days 7-8: Justification

THE APPENDIX

Lesson-Specific Activity Pages: Some lessons include specific activity pages for enhancing or completing the design challenges. They are found in the Appendix section.

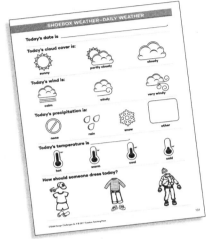

Blueprint Design Sheets: Every lesson requires students to first use the Individual Blueprint Design Sheet to sketch the design for their suggested prototype. Students will then describe their designs to the members of their team. After all team members have presented their designs, the team selects one design to use for building its prototype. This design is recorded on the Group Blueprint Design Sheet and presented to the teacher. Teachers may need to assist students in the labeling of the design and write a description of how the team plans to construct the prototype.

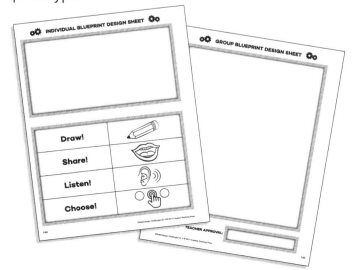

Rubric: A rubric for grading the STEAM challenges is included. This rubric focuses on the engineering process. However, it does not include a means to assess the justification components.

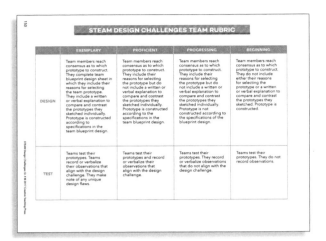

STEAM Job Cards: If your students are struggling with the collaboration process, try assigning them specific roles. Assigning students jobs often helps them better collaborate by giving them guidelines to follow. Suggestions for jobs are provided on the STEAM Job Cards found in the Appendix. Four students per team is recommended.

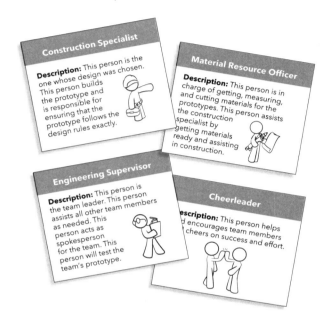

THE STANDARDS

SCIENCE

www.nextgenscience.org/search-standards-dci

The Next Generation Science Standards are arranged by disciplinary core ideas (DCI). When accessing these standards, search by standard and DCI. The standards are identified in the lessons by grade level and DCI. (e.g., 5-ESS3-1–Grade 5, Earth and Human Activity, Standard 1).

TECHNOLOGY

www.iste.org/standards

The International Society for Technology in Education (ISTE) publishes the national technology standards. Each of the standards is categorized into four main categories.

1. Creativity and innovation
2. Communication and collaboration
3. Research and information fluency
4. Critical thinking, problem solving, and decision making

Within each of these categories there are more specific indicators that are identified by a letter. Standards within the lessons will be indicated by the category (e.g., ISTE.1).

ENGINEERING

www.nextgenscience.org/search-standards-dci

The Next Generation Science Standards identify the engineering standards as well. They are categorized by the grade band of 3-5 (e.g., 3-5-ETS1-1).

ARTS

www.nationalartsstandards.org
www.corestandards.org/ELA-Literacy

The National Core Arts Standards are divided into four categories:

1. Creating
2. Performing/Presenting/Producing
3. Responding
4. Connecting

Each of these categories contains anchor standards. Within the lesson, the standards will be identified by the category and the anchor standard (e.g., Creating, Anchor Standard #1).

In addition to performance standards, the literacy standards are embedded throughout the lessons. Each lesson identifies specific English language arts (ELA) standards (e.g., CCSS.ELA-LITERACY.W.5.2).

MATH

www.corestandards.org/math

The Common Core Math Standards are divided into two categories:

1. Content
2. Practice

The content standards are those items such as computation and geometry. The practice standards are a framework for ensuring that students are practicing math in a meaningful and appropriate manner.

The content standards will be identified first in the Math Standards column and the Math Practice Standards will be underneath (e.g., CCSS.MATH.CONTENT.5.G.A.2–real world graphing and CCSS.MATH.PRACTICE.MP.4–model with mathematics).

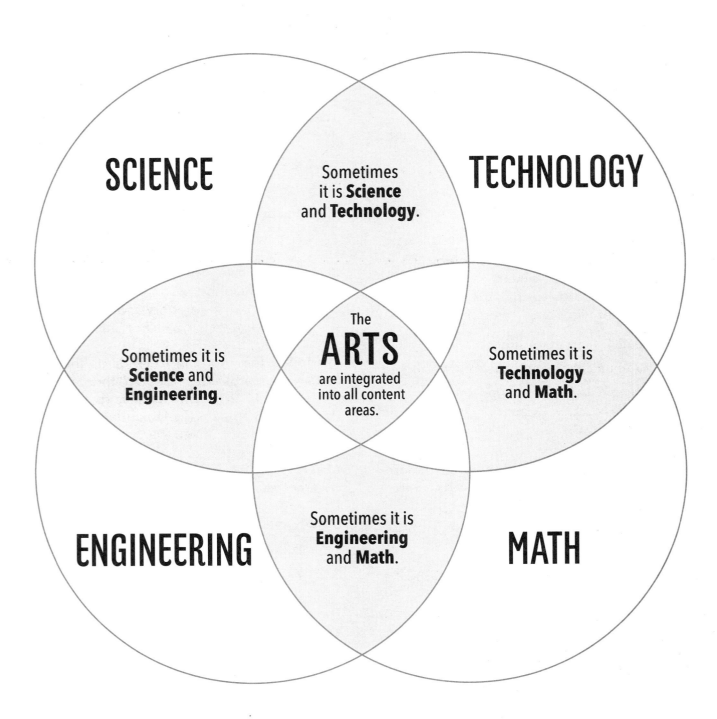

SCIENCE

TECHNOLOGY

Sometimes it is **Science** and **Technology**.

Sometimes it is **Science** and **Engineering**.

The
ARTS
are integrated into all content areas.

Sometimes it is **Technology** and **Math**.

ENGINEERING

Sometimes it is **Engineering** and **Math**.

MATH

Sometimes it is all five!

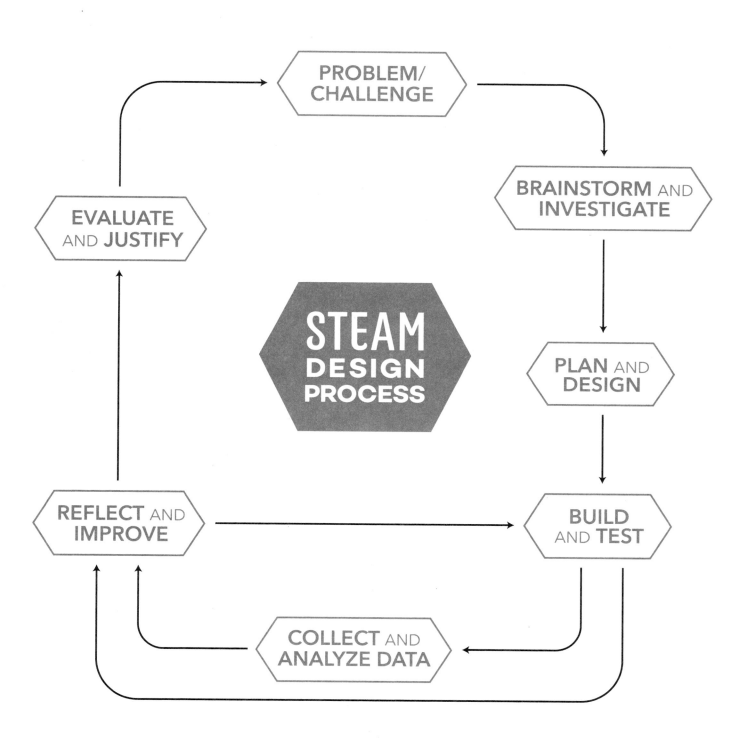

RECORDING INFORMATION IN A SCIENCE NOTEBOOK

Students will record their thinking, answer questions, make observations, and sketch ideas as they work through each design challenge. It is recommended that teachers have students designate a section of their regular science notebooks to these STEAM challenges or have students create a separate STEAM science notebook using a spiral notebook, a composition book, or lined pages stapled together. A generic science notebook cover sheet has been provided in the Appendix.

Have students set up their notebooks based upon the natural breaks in the lesson. Remind students to write the name of the design challenge at the top of the page in their notebooks each time they prepare their notebooks for a new challenge.

Pages 1–3 Background Information

- Teachers may lead a brief whole-group discussion that focuses on students' background knowledge of the concepts covered in the challenge. Students can write letters, words, symbols, or sketches in their notebook to help direct their thinking during the group discussion. Or teachers can give students an activity worksheet to complete and then glue into their notebooks.

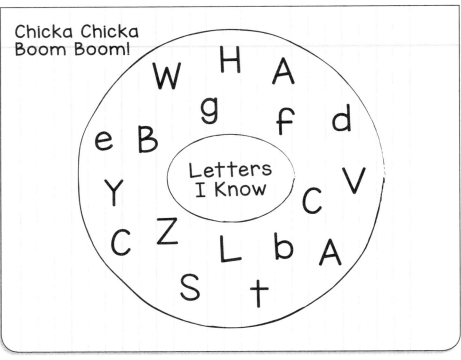

Page 1

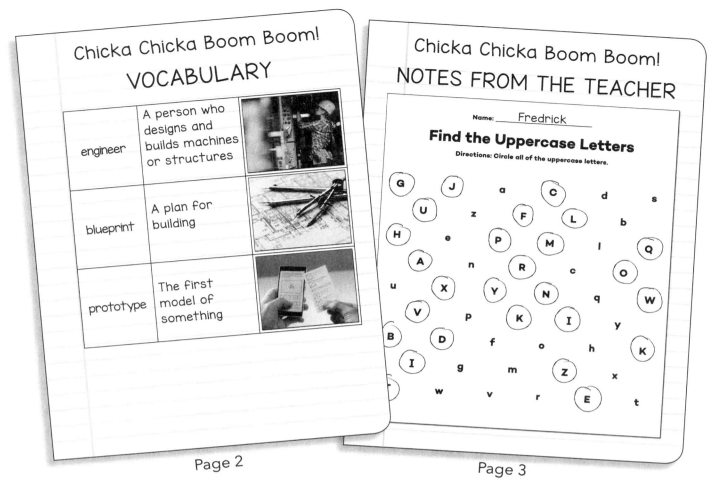

Page 2

Page 3

Students can cut out words and their definitions to match up by gluing the pieces into their notebooks. Teachers can also provide a sheet of definitions for students to cut out and glue into their notebooks and then write the word for each definition. Or make copies of the Vocabulary Sheet (page 146) and have students complete it and glue it into their notebooks.

Page 4 Dilemma and Mission

● Read the dilemma and mission aloud.

● Make copies of the dilemma and mission for students to glue into their notebooks to use as a reference.

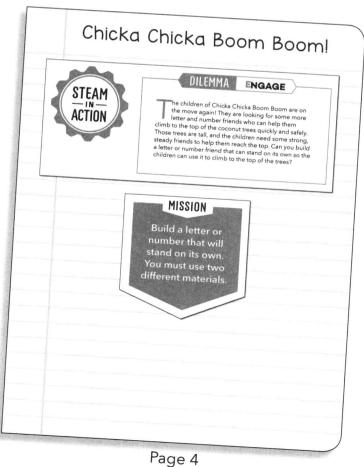

Page 4

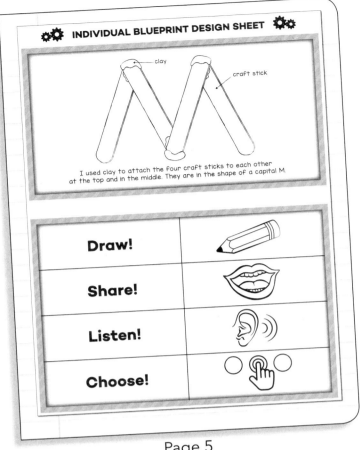

Page 5

Page 5 Blueprint Design

- Students draw their own suggested designs. Then students verbally explain and describe their designs to other members of the team and to the teacher.

- Teachers may need to assist students in labeling their designs and in writing descriptions of how the students plan to construct their prototypes.

- Teachers can make copies of the Individual Blueprint Design Sheet for students to complete and glue into their notebooks.

Engineering Task, Test Trial, Analyze, Redesign

- Teachers can lead a whole-class discussion during which they discuss the reflection questions and students' overall understanding of the concepts covered in the challenge.

- Students can also verbally summarize what they did during the challenge and tell one thing they learned.

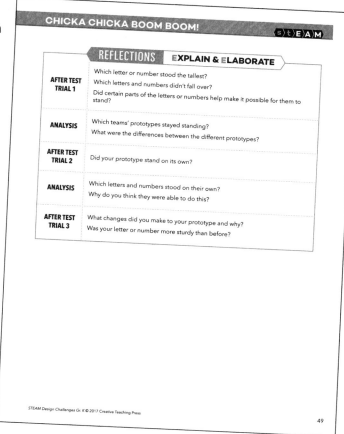

CHICKA CHICKA BOOM BOOM!   (S)(t)(E)(A)(M)

REFLECTIONS   EXPLAIN & ELABORATE

AFTER TEST TRIAL 1	Which letter or number stood the tallest? Which letters and numbers didn't fall over? Did certain parts of the letters or numbers help make it possible for them to stand?
ANALYSIS	Which teams' prototypes stayed standing? What were the differences between the different prototypes?
AFTER TEST TRIAL 2	Did your prototype stand on its own?
ANALYSIS	Which letters and numbers stood on their own? Why do you think they were able to do this?
AFTER TEST TRIAL 3	What changes did you make to your prototype and why? Was your letter or number more sturdy than before?

49

BEAR IS LOST!

3 HOURS
TIME FOR COMPLETION

STEAM m

SETTING —THE— STAGE

DESIGN CHALLENGE PURPOSE

Design a map of Bear's home and his surroundings.

TEACHER DEVELOPMENT

This particular science standard focuses on students using models to represent the relationship between the needs of different plants or animals and the places they live. Plants, animals, and their surroundings make up a **habitat**. Plants and animals have **needs** such as water, sunlight, food, air, and shelter. Many plants and animals have adapted to their surroundings in order to survive.

BEAR IS LOST!

STEAM

STUDENT DEVELOPMENT

Before beginning this lesson, review vocabulary terms (*habitat, needs, hibernate, survive*) and then read the books listed in literacy connections in order to prompt discussion with students. Ask questions such as *Why do bears sleep so much in winter? What is **hibernation**? What to animals need to do in order to prepare for hibernation? What happens when animals awake from hibernation? What are some things animals need in order to **survive**?*

STANDARDS

SCIENCE	TECHNOLOGY	ENGINEERING	ARTS	MATH	ELA
K-ESS3-1	ISTE.1	K-2-ETS1-1	Creating #1, #2, #3		CCSS.ELA-LITERACY.SL.K.1
		K-2-ETS1-2	Performing/ Presenting/ Producing #4, #5, #6		CCSS.ELA-LITERACY.W.K.3
			Responding #7, #8, #9		CCSS.ELA-LITERACY.W.K.6

SCIENCE & ENGINEERING PRACTICES

Developing and Using Models: Use a model to represent relationships in the natural world.

Obtaining, Evaluating, and Communicating Information: Communicate solutions with others in oral and/or written forms using models and/or drawings that provide detail about scientific ideas.

CROSSCUTTING CONCEPTS

Systems and System Models: Systems in the natural and designed world have parts that work together.

Interdependence of Science, Engineering, and Technology: People encounter questions about the natural world every day.

TARGET VOCABULARY

habitat

hibernate

needs

survive

MATERIALS

- poster board
- felt
- pipe cleaners
- construction paper
- newspapers
- magazines
- cotton balls
- paint
- markers
- cardboard
- yarn
- glue
- scissors

LITERACY CONNECTIONS

Bear Snores On
by Karma Wilson

Bear Feels Scared
by Karma Wilson

Hibernation Station
by Michelle Meadows

NOTES

STEAM
—IN—
ACTION

DILEMMA   **ENGAGE**

Bear wants to play a game of hide-and-seek after hibernating all winter. He has filled his belly with food, and now he is full of energy and ready for some fun! But Bear's friends are a little nervous. They know how scared Bear can get when he is lost, and they are worried he might get lost during the game. Can you help Bear by creating a map so he can always find his way home?

MISSION

Create a map that includes Bear's home and its surroundings.

Don't forget to include:

1. Bear's shelter
2. Bear's food sources
3. Bear's water sources
4. wildlife friends that live near Bear
5. map title
6. compass rose
7. legend

BLUEPRINT   **EXPLORE**

Provide the Individual Blueprint Design sheet, and ask students to sketch a design for a prototype they will describe to the other members of their team. After each team member has presented his or her design, the team as a whole will decide which prototype to construct and then draw it on the Group Blueprint Design sheet. Next, the team will present the design to the teacher for approval and for permission to retrieve their materials and begin construction.

ENGINEERING TASK **TEST TRIAL** **ANALYZE** **REDESIGN**

ENGINEERING TASK	TEST TRIAL	ANALYZE	REDESIGN
Each team will build a map of Bear's habitat and home. Include the things Bear needs to survive.	Teams will plan how they will share their maps to the rest of the class during their final trial.	Teams will take part in a gallery walk to observe the other designs and gather ideas to help improve their maps.	Teams can use a colored pencil to make adjustments to their original design sketches. Teams will present the changes to the teacher for approval before making changes to the protoypes. Then they can make changes to present their final maps.

HELPFUL TIPS

- After the Test Trial, have teams take a gallery walk to view other teams' designs for possible ideas to assist them in the Analyze and Redesign portions of the engineering design process.

- If teams are successful on the first try, encourage them to make their prototypes even more efficient. If it is a scenario in which this is not feasible, distribute team members to other teams to be a support for them in making their prototypes more efficient. Alternatively, at teacher discretion, move students on to the Justification portion of the lesson.

- If after the third test the final prototype is still unsuccessful, ask students how they would start over. These challenges are meant to have students build on what they originally designed. If the design proved to be unsuccessful, encourage a reflection/justification on what they would do if they were allowed to start again from scratch.

REFLECTIONS — EXPLAIN & ELABORATE

AFTER TEST TRIAL 1	What were some of the things your team's map included?
ANALYSIS	What were some things other teams put on their maps? What could you add to your map to make it more helpful to Bear?
AFTER TEST TRIAL 2	What new things were added to your team's map? How can they help Bear find his way home?
ANALYSIS	What were some similarities and differences between the different maps?
AFTER TEST TRIAL 3	What parts of the map would be most important for Bear? Why?

JUSTIFICATION — EVALUATE

ELA	*Note:* Students will need copies of the comic strip on page 129. Create a comic strip that tells about at least three things Bear might do to prepare to hibernate.
TECHNOLOGY	Use a publishing program to create an electronic version of your comic strip. *Note:* Visit the website listed on the inside front cover for a link to create an electronic version of your comic strip.

GRANDMA'S BIG MOVE

STEAM

SETTING —THE— STAGE

DESIGN CHALLENGE PURPOSE

Build a house that stands on stilts to avoid flooding.

TEACHER DEVELOPMENT

Some kinds of severe weather are more likely than others in a given region. Weather scientists (meteorologists) forecast severe weather so that communities can prepare for and respond to these events. Building houses on stilts is one way areas prone to flooding can prepare for high water.

Houses built on stilts are often used in coastal or subtropical locations. They can help protect the home from flooding and can sometimes allow builders to construct on rocky, steep, or otherwise unstable land. Stilt houses can also help keep out pests.

STUDENT DEVELOPMENT

Discuss types of severe weather and ways humans can prepare ahead of time in order to be safe. Explain to students that people in different parts of the world have different materials they can use to build their homes and other structures. They think about these materials and decide which would work best for where and how they want to live.

Allow time for students to view images of structures and discuss which structures would work best in certain locations.

Note: Visit the website listed on the inside front cover for a link to pictures and more information about different houses around the world.

STANDARDS

SCIENCE	TECHNOLOGY	ENGINEERING	ARTS	MATH	ELA
K-ESS3-2		K-2-ETS1-1	Creating #1		CCSS.ELA-LITERACY.SL.K.1
K-ESS3-3		K-2-ETS1-2	Creating #2		CCSS.ELA-LITERACY.W.K.3
		K-2-ETS1-3	Creating #3		

SCIENCE & ENGINEERING PRACTICES

Asking Questions and Designing Problems: Ask questions based on observations to find more information about the natural and/or designed world(s).

Developing and Using Models: Use a model to represent relationships in the natural world.

Obtaining, Evaluating, and Communicating Information: Communicate solutions with others in oral and/or written forms using models and/or drawings that provide detail about scientific ideas.

CROSSCUTTING CONCEPTS

Cause and Effect: Events have causes that generate observable patterns.

Systems and System Models: Systems in the natural world have parts that work together.

TARGET VOCABULARY

flood

forecast

model

prepare

severe

stilt house

weather

MATERIALS

- small empty milk cartons
- craft sticks
- straws
- modeling clay
- tape
- glue
- toothpicks
- empty cereal boxes
- construction paper
- wooden dowels
- scissors
- aluminum tray filled with 2 in. of water

LITERACY CONNECTIONS

Look at That Building!: A First Book of Structures by Scot Ritchie

Little Red Riding Hood by James Marshall

NOTES

STEAM
— IN —
ACTION

DILEMMA ENGAGE

Little Red Riding Hood is worried about her grandmother after her last run-in with Big Bad Wolf. Her grandmother lives alone, and although Little Red visits Grandmother frequently, she does not want Grandmother living alone in the forest. Little Red wants to help build her grandmother a new house by the beach, far from wolves and high enough off the ground to keep it safe from flooding. Little Red needs your help designing a safe home for Grandmother.

MISSION

Build a house on stilts that can stand on its own, high enough so that it does not touch the water.

BLUEPRINT EXPLORE

Provide the Individual Blueprint Design sheet, and ask students to sketch a design for a prototype they will describe to the other members of their team. After each team member has presented his or her design, the team as a whole will decide which prototype to construct and then draw it on the Group Blueprint Design sheet. Next, the team will present the design to the teacher for approval and for permission to retrieve their materials and begin construction.

ENGINEERING TASK

Each team will build a house on stilts that can stand on its own when placed in a tub filled with water.

TEST TRIAL

Each team will place its house in a tub filled with 2 in. of water. The house must sit higher than the water and stand on its own.

ANALYZE

Teams will talk about their results, and discuss the successful design elements with the class.

Teams should be allowed to observe the other designs to gather ideas, reflect, and make changes in order to improve their prototypes.

REDESIGN

Teams can use a colored pencil to make adjustments to their original design sketches. Teams will present the changes to the teacher for approval before making changes to the prototypes. Then they can get new supplies to rebuild and retest their prototypes.

HELPFUL TIPS

- After the Test Trial, have teams take a gallery walk to view other teams' designs for possible ideas to assist them in the Analyze and Redesign portions of the engineering design process.

- If teams are successful on the first try, encourage them to make their prototypes even more efficient. If it is a scenario in which this is not feasible, distribute team members to other teams to be a support for them in making their prototypes more efficient. Alternatively, at teacher discretion, move students on to the Justification portion of the lesson.

- If after the third test the final prototype is still unsuccessful, ask students how they would start over. These challenges are meant to have students build on what they originally designed. If the design proved to be unsuccessful, encourage a reflection/justification on what they would do if they were allowed to start again from scratch.

REFLECTIONS EXPLAIN & ELABORATE

AFTER TEST TRIAL 1	Was your house able to stand on its own? Were the stilts high enough to keep the house from touching the water?
ANALYSIS	What parts of your design were most successful? What could you change to improve your prototype?
AFTER TEST TRIAL 2	Did your changes improve your house? Was it able to stand on its own in this trial?
ANALYSIS	Which teams' houses stood on their own above the water? What were some similarities and differences between your prototype and the prototypes of the other teams?
AFTER TEST TRIAL 3	Were the changes you made to your design helpful? Why or why not?

JUSTIFICATION EVALUATE

ARTS	*Note:* Students will need a copy of the sign on page 130. Use this sign when you display your students' prototypes, or have them create their own versions as a justification project. Decorate Grandma's house. Then make a "No Trespassing" sign to keep unwanted visitors away.
ELA	Draw, tell, or write a retelling of the story of "Little Red Riding Hood" in your own words.

SHOEBOX WEATHER

1 HOUR

TIME FOR COMPLETION

10-20 MINS DAILY
20 MINS WEEKLY

S t e A M

SETTING
—THE—
STAGE

DESIGN CHALLENGE PURPOSE

Track the weather for the month, and use that data to predict the weather for the following month.

TEACHER DEVELOPMENT

Learning about the **weather** in a different part of the country helps students better understand different types of weather they are not usually exposed to. For example, students in the South usually do not experience snow, sleet, or storms associated with very low temperatures. Introducing students to the climates of other regions is helpful for this challenge.

Find a teacher in another climate zone to partner with on this project. Each class will receive a decorated weather box from the partner classroom each month.

STEAM Design Challenges Gr. K © 2017 Creative Teaching Press

STUDENT DEVELOPMENT

Introduce the different temperature measurement scales (i.e., Celsius and Fahrenheit) before this challenge. Students will need to know the following vocabulary: **cloud cover**, **rain**, **temperature**, **sunlight**, and **wind**.

cloud cover: the sky is covered with mostly clouds and is normally described in a weather report as mostly cloudy or partly cloudy

rain: the water that falls from the clouds when the temperature is above freezing

temperature: measurement of how hot or cold a place is

sunlight: the light that we receive from the sun

wind: movement of air

Students should be introduced to how weather forecasters (meteorologists) observe and notice patterns for weather conditions in certain areas over long periods of time. Examples of observations include differences in temperatures throughout the day and at different times of the year, the number of sunny days versus cloudy days in a given month, and average rainfall in a given month. Discuss with students how they can use their senses to make observations about the weather.

STANDARDS

SCIENCE	TECHNOLOGY	ENGINEERING	ARTS	MATH	ELA
K-ESS2-1			Creating #1	CCSS.MATH.CONTENT.K.CC.B.4	CCSS.ELA-LITERACY.W.K-2
			Creating #2	CCSS.MATH.CONTENT.K.CC.B.5	CCSS.ELA-LITERACY.W.K-3
			Creating #3		CCSS.ELA-LITERACY.W.K.7

SCIENCE & ENGINEERING PRACTICES

Analyzing and Interpreting Data: Use observations (firsthand or from media) to describe patterns in the natural world in order to answer scientific questions.

CROSSCUTTING CONCEPTS

Patterns: Patterns in the natural world can be observed, used to describe phenomena, and used as evidence.

TARGET VOCABULARY

cloudy (cloud cover)

patterns

rain

snow

sunlight

sunny

temperature

warm

weather

wind

MATERIALS

- construction paper
- shoeboxes
- crayons
- markers
- outdoor thermometer
- daily weather sheet (page 131)
- weekly weather sheet (page 132)

LITERACY CONNECTIONS

The Kids' Book of Weather Forecasting: Build a Weather Station, "Read" the Sky and Make Predictions!
by Mark Breen and Kathleen Friestad

NOTES

STEAM —IN— ACTION

DILEMMA ENGAGE

Note: Replace the names in the dilemma with your name and with the names of the teacher and school you are exchanging information with.

Ms. Cloudburst is a kindergarten teacher at Weathermaker Elementary School. Ms. Cloudburst has a teacher friend, Ms. Drizzle, who also teaches kindergarten. They live in different states, but they want their students to be pen pals and to teach each other about where they live. They decide to have students record the weather and tell about it. Ms. Cloudburst thinks that her students may not be able to keep track of the weather and wants to have some kindergarteners try it. Can you try it out to see if you can keep track of the weather?

MISSION

Record the weather each day for a month. Then use that data to predict the weather for the following month.

BLUEPRINT EXPLORE

Provide the Individual Blueprint Design sheet, and ask students to sketch a design for a prototype they will describe to the other members of their team. After each team member has presented his or her design, the team as a whole will decide which prototype to construct and then draw it on the Group Blueprint Design sheet. Next, the team will present the design to the teacher for approval and for permission to retrieve their materials and begin construction.

ENGINEERING TASK	TEST TRIAL	ANALYZE	REDESIGN

ENGINEERING TASK

The class will decorate a box that contains the weather data collected over the course of a month and the weather predictions for the following month.

- Center Group Work: Data collection and analysis of the daily weather sheet
  Daily: 10–20 minutes
- Whole Class Instruction: Weekly weather count and end-of-the-month weather box
  Weekly: 20 minutes
- Center Group Work: Each team takes turns decorating a side of the weather box to reflect the weather data collected for the month. Then all teams place their weather sheets inside the box.
  Final project: 1 hour

TEST TRIAL

Individual students record the daily weather data and then compare their data with their team members' data. Team members use this information and work together to determine the weekly weather data.

ANALYZE

Does your daily weather data match the data collected by the other members of your team?

REDESIGN

Team members should be allowed to share their weather data with one another and then make adjustments based on their findings.

 # HELPFUL TIPS

- After the Test Trial, have teams take a gallery walk to view other teams' designs for possible ideas to assist them in the Analyze and Redesign portions of the engineering design process.

- If teams are successful on the first try, encourage them to make their prototypes even more efficient. If it is a scenario in which this is not feasible, distribute team members to other teams to be a support for them in making their prototypes more efficient. Alternatively, at teacher discretion, move students on to the Justification portion of the lesson.

- If after the third test the final prototype is still unsuccessful, ask students how they would start over. These challenges are meant to have students build on what they originally designed. If the design proved to be unsuccessful, encourage a reflection/justification on what they would do if they were allowed to start again from scratch.

REFLECTIONS   EXPLAIN & ELABORATE

AFTER TEST TRIAL 1	Did your data match the data of the rest of the class for that week's daily weather collection?
ANALYSIS	What was different about your data from your classmates' data?
AFTER TEST TRIAL 2	Did your data collection match your classmates' data?
ANALYSIS	Were you able to correctly collect all of the data this week? Did you work with a partner?
AFTER TEST TRIAL 3	Did your data match the class data?

JUSTIFICATION   EVALUATE

ARTS	Students will decorate the weather box to match that month's collected weather data. Students can draw pictures of what the weather was mostly like for that month and include the pictures inside the box.
ELA	Students use a combination of drawing, dictating, and writing to compose informative/explanatory description of that month's weather.

SWINE SHELTER

2 HOURS
TIME FOR COMPLETION

SETTING
—THE—
STAGE

DESIGN CHALLENGE PURPOSE

Build a model of a house that is protected from a type of dangerous weather.

TEACHER DEVELOPMENT

For this lesson, you will need to research the types of hazardous weather that are possible in your area. Also research the danger they pose for houses. Discuss with students a specific disaster and show them pictures of different types of protection, such as a basement for tornados, shutters for hurricanes, and sandbags for flooding.

STUDENT DEVELOPMENT

Students will need background information about dangerous storms and natural disasters that affect your area, such as earthquakes, tornadoes, hurricanes, blizzards, floods, tsunamis, or dangerous thunderstorms.

Lesson Idea: Complete the 2-liter bottle tornado demonstration (below) and discuss the power and danger of a tornado.

The teacher will fill one 2-liter bottle with water and use duct tape and a washer to connect another 2-liter bottle upside down on top of the first bottle. To enhance the tornado effect, small pieces of foil or colored paper, small amounts of dish soap, or food coloring can be added to the water inside the bottle before sealing. Have students turn the bottle upside down after sealing and take turns swirling the bottle to create a tornado effect when the water drains from one bottle to the next.

Note: Visit the website listed on the inside front cover for a link to more information about creating a tornado in a bottle.

STANDARDS

SCIENCE	TECHNOLOGY	ENGINEERING	ARTS	MATH	ELA
K-ESS3-2		K-2-ETS1-1	Creating #1		CCSS.ELA-LITERACY.SL.K.5
		K-2-ETS1-2	Creating #2		CCSS.ELA-LITERACY.SL.K.3
		K-2-ETS1-3	Creating #3		CCSS.ELA-LITERACY.SL.K.1.A
					CCSS.ELA-LITERACY.W.K.2

SCIENCE & ENGINEERING PRACTICES

Asking Questions and Defining Problems: Ask questions based on observations to find more information about the natural and/or designed world(s).

Obtaining, Evaluating, and Communicating Information: Read grade-appropriate texts and/or use media to obtain scientific information to describe patterns in the natural world.

CROSSCUTTING CONCEPTS

Interdependence of Science, Engineering, and Technology: People encounter questions about the natural world every day.

TARGET VOCABULARY

blizzard

earthquake

flood

hurricane

thunderstorm

tornado

tsunami

MATERIALS

- pieces of cardboard
- square-bottomed empty milk cartons
- craft sticks
- straws
- pebbles
- cotton balls
- toothpicks
- paper plates
- scissors
- tape
- glue

LITERACY CONNECTIONS

The Three Little Pigs by RH Disney

Tornado!: The Story Behind These Twisting, Turning, Spinning, and Spiraling Storms by Judy Fradin and Dennis Fradin

Extreme Weather: Surviving Tornadoes, Sandstorms, Hailstorms, Blizzards, Hurricanes, and More! by Thomas M. Kostigen

NOTES

STEAM
—IN—
ACTION

DILEMMA ENGAGE

The three pigs lived happily together in the same house until they discovered that some dangerous weather was on its way to their town. The storm was a (insert a storm type from your area), and it was expected to arrive very soon. The pigs need your help! Build a model of their house and include ways their house can be protected from the storm.

MISSION

Build a model of a house showing the way the house will be protected from dangerous weather or a natural disaster.

BLUEPRINT EXPLORE

Provide the Individual Blueprint Design sheet, and ask students to sketch a design for a prototype they will describe to the other members of their team. After each team member has presented his or her design, the team as a whole will decide which prototype to construct and then draw it on the Group Blueprint Design sheet. Next, the team will present the design to the teacher for approval and for permission to retrieve their materials and begin construction.

ENGINEERING TASK	TEST TRIAL	ANALYZE	REDESIGN
Prior to the challenge, the teacher should select a type of dangerous weather or natural disaster that all teams will build prototypes to protect against. Teams will build a model of a home that includes protection against the predetermined hazardous weather or natural disaster.	Each team will present its prototype to another team, explaining the protection that was created and how it would keep the house safe.	Each team will receive feedback from its partner team and use that information to redesign and make improvements to the prototype. Teams should be allowed to observe the other designs to gather ideas, reflect, and make changes in order to improve their prototypes.	Teams can use a colored pencil to make adjustments to their original design sketches. Teams will present the changes to the teacher for approval before making changes to the prototypes. Then they can get new supplies to rebuild and retest their prototypes.

HELPFUL TIPS

- After the Test Trial, have teams take a gallery walk to view other teams' designs for possible ideas to assist them in the Analyze and Redesign portions of the engineering design process.

- If teams are successful on the first try, encourage them to make their prototypes even more efficient. If it is a scenario in which this is not feasible, distribute team members to other teams to be a support for them in making their prototypes more efficient. Alternatively, at teacher discretion, move students on to the Justification portion of the lesson.

- If after the third test the final prototype is still unsuccessful, ask students how they would start over. These challenges are meant to have students build on what they originally designed. If the design proved to be unsuccessful, encourage a reflection/justification on what they would do if they were allowed to start again from scratch.

REFLECTIONS — EXPLAIN & ELABORATE

AFTER TEST TRIAL 1	Were you able to explain how your design would protect the house?
ANALYSIS	What suggestions did the other team have to improve your design? Do you need to change anything after explaining your ideas to the other team?
AFTER TEST TRIAL 2	Were you able to make changes that helped improve your model?
ANALYSIS	Do you need to make any more changes to help protect the house?
AFTER TEST TRIAL 3	Were you able to explain how your design would protect the house?

JUSTIFICATION — EVALUATE

ELA	*Note:* Students will need a copy of the pamphlet on page 133-134. If students need more room to write, enlarge copies of the page and print on 11"x17" paper (zoom ratio 1.294 or 129%). Create a pamphlet about how your design protected the pigs' house.
ARTS	Create a safety poster telling others how they can prepare for dangerous weather.

CHICKA CHICKA BOOM BOOM!

st**EAM**

SETTING
—THE—
STAGE

DESIGN CHALLENGE PURPOSE

Design and construct a letter or number that stands on its own.

TEACHER DEVELOPMENT

The lesson requires students to apply the steps of the engineering design process to complete the challenge.

Refer to the STEAM design process diagram (page 15) for a description of each step.

STUDENT DEVELOPMENT

This is a great lesson for teaching the engineering process to students. Introduce the words **blueprint**, **design**, **engineer**, and **prototype** to your students. Teach them how to collaborate and work as a team. Use the STEAM job cards (page 144) to assign jobs to students to demonstrate the importance of working together.

STANDARDS

SCIENCE	TECHNOLOGY	ENGINEERING	ARTS	MATH	ELA
		K-2-ETS1-1	Creating #1	MATH. CONTENT.K.CC.A.3	CCSS.ELA-LITERACY.SL.K.1
		K-2-ETS1-2			CCSS.ELA-LITERACY.W.K.3
		K-2-ETS1-3			

SCIENCE & ENGINEERING PRACTICES

Developing and Using Models: Use a model to represent relationships in the natural world.

Obtaining, Evaluating, and Communicating Information: Communicate solutions with others in oral and/or written forms using models and/or drawings that provide detail about scientific ideas.

CROSSCUTTING CONCEPTS

Cause and Effect: Events have causes that generate observable patterns.

Systems and System Models: Systems in the natural and designed world have parts that work together.

TARGET VOCABULARY

blueprint
design
engineer
prototype

MATERIALS

- modeling clay
- pieces of cardboard
- straws
- construction paper
- pipe cleaners
- tape
- craft sticks
- string
- scissors

LITERACY CONNECTIONS

Chicka Chicka Boom Boom
by Bill Martin Jr.
and John Archambault

Chicka Chicka 1, 2, 3
by Bill Martin Jr. and
Michael Sampson

NOTES

STEAM
—IN—
ACTION

DILEMMA ENGAGE

The children of Chicka Chicka Boom Boom are on the move again! They are looking for some more letter and number friends who can help them climb to the top of the coconut trees quickly and safely. Those trees are tall, and the children need some strong, steady friends to help them reach the top. Can you build a letter or number friend that can stand on its own so the children can use it to climb to the top of the trees?

MISSION

Build a letter or number that will stand on its own. You must use two different materials.

BLUEPRINT EXPLORE

Provide the Individual Blueprint Design sheet, and ask students to sketch a design for a prototype they will describe to the other members of their team. After each team member has presented his or her design, the team as a whole will decide which prototype to construct and then draw it on the Group Blueprint Design sheet. Next, the team will present the design to the teacher for approval and for permission to retrieve their materials and begin construction.

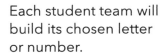

ENGINEERING TASK

Each student team will build its chosen letter or number.

Extension Idea: Build a coconut tree that will stand up by itself. The tree must remain standing when the letters and numbers are placed on it.

TEST TRIAL

Each team will test its prototype to see if it stands without support. Ensure that students make observations about what happened during the other teams' trials.

ANALYZE

Teams will talk about their results, and discuss the successful design elements with the class.

Teams should be allowed to observe the other designs to gather ideas, reflect, and make changes in order to improve their prototypes.

REDESIGN

Teams can use a colored pencil to make adjustments to their original design sketches. Teams will present the changes to the teacher for approval before making changes to the prototypes. Then they can get new supplies to rebuild and retest their prototypes.

HELPFUL TIPS

- After the Test Trial, have teams take a gallery walk to view other teams' designs for possible ideas to assist them in the Analyze and Redesign portions of the engineering design process.

- If teams are successful on the first try, encourage them to make their prototypes even more efficient. If it is a scenario in which this is not feasible, distribute team members to other teams to be a support for them in making their prototypes more efficient. Alternatively, at teacher discretion, move students on to the Justification portion of the lesson.

- If after the third test the final prototype is still unsuccessful, ask students how they would start over. These challenges are meant to have students build on what they originally designed. If the design proved to be unsuccessful, encourage a reflection/justification on what they would do if they were allowed to start again from scratch.

REFLECTIONS — EXPLAIN & ELABORATE

AFTER TEST TRIAL 1	Which letter or number stood the tallest? Which letters and numbers didn't fall over? Did certain parts of the letters or numbers help make it possible for them to stand?
ANALYSIS	Which teams' prototypes stayed standing? What were the differences between the different prototypes?
AFTER TEST TRIAL 2	Did your prototype stand on its own?
ANALYSIS	Which letters and numbers stood on their own? Why do you think they were able to do this?
AFTER TEST TRIAL 3	What changes did you make to your prototype and why? Was your letter or number more sturdy than before?

JUSTIFICATION — EVALUATE

ELA	Draw, tell, or write an adventure about the children of Chicka Chicka Boom Boom. Tell about three things that happened and how the children reacted to the events.

MISCHIEVOUS MONKEYS

2-3 HOURS

TIME FOR COMPLETION

SETTING
— THE —
STAGE

DESIGN CHALLENGE PURPOSE

Construct a protective suit for an egg to help it survive a fall from a desk.

TEACHER DEVELOPMENT

The lesson requires students to apply the steps of the engineering design process to complete the challenge.

Refer to the STEAM design process diagram (page 15) for a description of each step.

STEAM Design Challenges Gr. K © 2017 Creative Teaching Press

STUDENT DEVELOPMENT

This is a great lesson for teaching the engineering process to students. Introduce the words **blueprint**, **design**, **engineer**, and **prototype** to your students. Teach them how to collaborate and work as a team. Use the STEAM job cards (page 144) to assign jobs to students to demonstrate the importance of working together.

STANDARDS

SCIENCE	TECHNOLOGY	ENGINEERING	ARTS	MATH	ELA
	ISTE.1	K-2-ETS1-1	Creating #1		CCSS.ELA-LITERACY.SL.K.1
		K-2-ETS1-2			CCSS.ELA-LITERACY.W.K.3
		K-2-ETS1-3			

SCIENCE & ENGINEERING PRACTICES

Developing and Using Models: Use a model to represent relationships in the natural world.

Obtaining, Evaluating, and Communicating Information: Communicate solutions with others in oral and/or written forms using models and/or drawings that provide detail about scientific ideas.

CROSSCUTTING CONCEPTS

Cause and Effect: Events have causes that generate observable patterns.

Systems and System Models: Systems in the natural and designed world have parts that work together.

TARGET VOCABULARY

blueprint

design

engineer

prototype

MATERIALS

- straws
- small empty milk cartons
- paper cups
- toothpicks
- tape
- hard-boiled eggs
- scissors

LITERACY CONNECTIONS

Five Little Monkeys Jumping on the Bed by Eileen Christelow

Naughty Little Monkeys by Jim Aylesworth

NOTES

s/T/E/A/m

DILEMMA ENGAGE

Five little monkeys are at it again! They were left at home while Mama went out for some groceries. These five little monkeys want to try out some new tricks as they jump on the bed, but they remember what Mama said, "No more monkeys jumping on the bed!"

Help the monkeys practice their new tricks without getting hurt. Design a suit that will protect them if they fall off the bed.

MISSION

Design a protective suit to protect a monkey (egg) during a fall off the bed (desk).

BLUEPRINT EXPLORE

Provide the Individual Blueprint Design sheet, and ask students to sketch a design for a prototype they will describe to the other members of their team. After each team member has presented his or her design, the team as a whole will decide which prototype to construct and then draw it on the Group Blueprint Design sheet. Next, the team will present the design to the teacher for approval and for permission to retrieve their materials and begin construction.

ENGINEERING TASK

 TEST TRIAL

 ANALYZE

 REDESIGN

ENGINEERING TASK

Each team will construct a protective suit for an egg to withstand a fall from the top of a desk.

Note: Place newspaper or plastic on the floor below the desk prior to testing.

TEST TRIAL

Each team will place its egg in the protective suit and place it on the edge of the desk. The team will knock its egg off the table and check for any damage after the fall.

ANALYZE

Teams will talk about their results and discuss the successful design elements with the class.

Teams should be allowed to observe the other designs to gather ideas, reflect, and make changes in order to improve their prototypes.

REDESIGN

Teams can use a colored pencil to make adjustments to their original design sketches. Teams will present the changes to the teacher for approval before making changes to the prototypes. Then they can get new supplies to rebuild and retest their prototypes.

 HELPFUL TIPS

- After the Test Trial, have teams take a gallery walk to view other teams' designs for possible ideas to assist them in the Analyze and Redesign portions of the engineering design process.

- If teams are successful on the first try, encourage them to make their prototypes even more efficient. If it is a scenario in which this is not feasible, distribute team members to other teams to be a support for them in making their prototypes more efficient. Alternatively, at teacher discretion, move students on to the Justification portion of the lesson.

- If after the third test the final prototype is still unsuccessful, ask students how they would start over. These challenges are meant to have students build on what they originally designed. If the design proved to be unsuccessful, encourage a reflection/justification on what they would do if they were allowed to start again from scratch.

REFLECTIONS — EXPLAIN & ELABORATE

AFTER TEST TRIAL 1	Did your protective suit stay on the egg? Was there any damage to your egg?
ANALYSIS	What material worked best? What were some similarities and differences between the different suit prototypes?
AFTER TEST TRIAL 2	Was there any damage to your egg this time?
ANALYSIS	What changes did you make to your prototype this time around? Did these changes keep your egg safe?
AFTER TEST TRIAL 3	Which team's suit worked best?

JUSTIFICATION — EVALUATE

TECHNOLOGY	Take pictures of your prototype during each test trial. With teacher support, add the pictures to a slide show. Then present it to the class and tell the class what you learned.
ARTS	Design and decorate a caution sign to post near your bed.
ELA	Write, tell, or draw a story about the mischievous monkeys getting into trouble when Mama leaves them home alone.

PESKY RABBITS!

2-3 HOURS

TIME FOR COMPLETION

s t E A m

SETTING —THE— STAGE

DESIGN CHALLENGE PURPOSE

Design a fence that will keep intruders out of the vegetable garden.

TEACHER DEVELOPMENT

The lesson requires students to apply the steps of the engineering design process to complete the challenge.

Refer to the STEAM design process diagram (page 15) for a description of each step.

STUDENT DEVELOPMENT

This is a great lesson for teaching the engineering process to students. Introduce the words **blueprint**, **design**, **engineer**, and **prototype** to your students. Teach them how to collaborate and work as a team. Use the STEAM job cards (page 144) to assign jobs to students to demonstrate the importance of working together.

STANDARDS

SCIENCE	TECHNOLOGY	ENGINEERING	ARTS	MATH	ELA
		K-2-ETS1-1	Creating #1		CCSS.ELA-LITERACY.SL.K.1
		K-2-ETS1-2			CCSS.ELA-LITERACY.W.K.3
		K-2-ETS1-3			

SCIENCE & ENGINEERING PRACTICES

Developing and Using Models: Use a model to represent relationships in the natural world.

Obtaining, Evaluating, and Communicating Information: Communicate solutions with others in oral and/or written forms using models and/or drawings that provide detail about scientific ideas.

CROSSCUTTING CONCEPTS

Cause and Effect: Events have causes that generate observable patterns.

Systems and System Models: Systems in the natural and designed world have parts that work together.

TARGET VOCABULARY

blueprint

design

engineer

prototype

MATERIALS

- toothpicks
- modeling clay
- yarn
- 6 craft sticks
- masking tape
- construction paper
- wind-up car
- scissors

LITERACY CONNECTIONS

Muncha! Muncha! Muncha!
by Candace Fleming

The Tale of Peter Rabbit
by Beatrix Potter

NOTES

DILEMMA — ENGAGE

Mr. McGreely is known all around town for the delicious vegetables from his garden. He wants to help some of his neighbors start their own gardens, but he is worried about the pesky rabbits that sneak into the garden to eat his vegetables. He knows that a strong, sturdy fence will do the job, but he needs help with the design. Help Mr. McGreely design a fence to protect the neighborhood gardens.

MISSION

Construct a fence to protect a vegetable garden (seed in cup). The fence must stay standing when a pest (toy car) runs into it.

BLUEPRINT — EXPLORE

Provide the Individual Blueprint Design sheet, and ask students to sketch a design for a prototype they will describe to the other members of their team. After each team member has presented his or her design, the team as a whole will decide which prototype to construct and then draw it on the Group Blueprint Design sheet. Next, the team will present the design to the teacher for approval and for permission to retrieve their materials and begin construction.

ENGINEERING TASK TEST TRIAL ANALYZE REDESIGN

ENGINEERING TASK	TEST TRIAL	ANALYZE	REDESIGN
Each team will build a fence to surround a model vegetable garden (plastic cup with vegetable seeds). The fence must withstand the force of a moving pest.

Note: Teacher can prepare a cup with soil and vegetable seeds prior to the challenge or use plastic toy vegetables during the test trials. | Teams will use a wind-up car to test the strength of their fences.

Note: Teacher should use a piece of tape to mark the starting point for the toy car. | Teams will talk about their results and discuss the successful design elements with the class.

Teams should be allowed to observe the other designs to gather ideas, reflect, and make changes in order to improve their prototypes. | Teams can use a colored pencil to make adjustments to their original design sketches. Teams will present the changes to the teacher for approval before making changes to the prototypes. Then they can get new supplies to rebuild and retest their prototypes. |

HELPFUL TIPS

- After the Test Trial, have teams take a gallery walk to view other teams' designs for possible ideas to assist them in the Analyze and Redesign portions of the engineering design process.

- If teams are successful on the first try, encourage them to make their prototypes even more efficient. If it is a scenario in which this is not feasible, distribute team members to other teams to be a support for them in making their prototypes more efficient. Alternatively, at teacher discretion, move students on to the Justification portion of the lesson.

- If after the third test the final prototype is still unsuccessful, ask students how they would start over. These challenges are meant to have students build on what they originally designed. If the design proved to be unsuccessful, encourage a reflection/justification on what they would do if they were allowed to start again from scratch.

REFLECTIONS   **EXPLAIN & ELABORATE**

AFTER TEST TRIAL 1	Which prototype fence was the tallest? Which was the strongest? What materials do you think helped make this fence strong?
ANALYSIS	What were the differences between the different fence prototypes?
AFTER TEST TRIAL 2	Did your fence stand on its own? Was there any damage caused to your fence?
ANALYSIS	Which materials do you think make the strongest fence?
AFTER TEST TRIAL 3	What changes did you make to your prototype and why? Was your final product stronger than your first?

JUSTIFICATION   **EVALUATE**

ARTS	Decorate your fence.
ELA	Draw, tell, or write a story about a plan the rabbits came up with to sneak inside the fence.

SAVE THE GINGERBREAD MAN!

s t E A m

1-2 HOURS

TIME FOR COMPLETION

SETTING —THE— STAGE

DESIGN CHALLENGE PURPOSE

Design a bridge to support the weight of the Gingerbread Man.

TEACHER DEVELOPMENT

The lesson requires students to apply the steps of the engineering design process to complete the challenge.

Refer to the STEAM design process diagram (page 15) for a description of each step.

STUDENT DEVELOPMENT

This is a great lesson for teaching the engineering process to students. Introduce the words **blueprint**, **design**, **engineer**, and **prototype** to your students. Teach them how to collaborate and work as a team. Use the STEAM job cards (page 144) to assign jobs to students to demonstrate the importance of working together.

Students will need to have some understanding about what can happen when **weight** is put on objects.

STANDARDS

SCIENCE	TECHNOLOGY	ENGINEERING	ARTS	MATH	ELA
		K-2-ETS1-1	Creating #1		CCSS.ELA-LITERACY.SL.K.1
		K-2-ETS1-2	Creating #2		CCSS.ELA-LITERACY.W.K.3
		K-2-ETS1-3	Creating #3		

SCIENCE & ENGINEERING PRACTICES

Asking Questions and Defining Problems: Define a simple problem that can be solved through the development of a new or improved object or tool.

Developing and Using Models: Develop a simple model based on evidence to represent a proposed object or tool.

Constructing Explanations and Designing Solutions: Use tools and/or materials to design and/or build a device that solves a specific problem or a solution to a specific problem.

CROSSCUTTING CONCEPTS

Structure and Function: The shape and stability of structures of natural and designed objects are related to their function.

TARGET VOCABULARY

blueprint
bridge
design
engineer
prototype
weight

MATERIALS

- pipe cleaners
- dry spaghetti
- toothpicks
- mini marshmallows
- tape
- wooden skewers
- string
- scissors
- small toy (to represent the Gingerbread Man)
- stopwatch

LITERACY CONNECTIONS

The Gingerbread Man by Karen Schmidt

The Gingerbread Man by Parragon Books

Bridges: Amazing Structures to Design, Build & Test by Carol A. Johmann and Elizabeth Rieth

NOTES

STEAM
— IN —
ACTION

DILEMMA ENGAGE

The Gingerbread Man needs your help! He has been running as fast as he can, but there's a problem. He just came upon a wide river with no way to cross. He is being chased and must cross the river to escape. If he gets wet, he will fall apart! He needs a way to cross the river and keep himself dry so he can escape. Help the Gingerbread Man build a bridge to cross the river.

MISSION

Follow these rules to build a bridge for the Gingerbread Man:

- You may only use the materials provided.

- The bridge must hold the weight of the gingerbread man (small toy).

- Your bridge must stand without being crushed.

BLUEPRINT EXPLORE

Provide the Individual Blueprint Design sheet, and ask students to sketch a design for a prototype they will describe to the other members of their team. After each team member has presented his or her design, the team as a whole will decide which prototype to construct and then draw it on the Group Blueprint Design sheet. Next, the team will present the design to the teacher for approval and for permission to retrieve their materials and begin construction.

ENGINEERING TASK	TEST TRIAL	ANALYZE	REDESIGN
Each team will construct a bridge that can support the weight of a small toy.	Each team will place a small toy on its bridge to see if the bridge will hold the weight of the toy for one minute.	Teams will talk about their results and discuss the successful design elements with the class. Teams should be allowed to observe the other designs to gather ideas, reflect, and make changes in order to improve their prototypes.	Teams can use a colored pencil to make adjustments to their original design sketches. Teams will present the changes to the teacher for approval before making changes to the prototypes. Then they can get new supplies to rebuild and retest their prototypes.

 HELPFUL TIPS

- After the Test Trial, have teams take a gallery walk to view other teams' designs for possible ideas to assist them in the Analyze and Redesign portions of the engineering design process.

- If teams are successful on the first try, encourage them to make their prototypes even more efficient. If it is a scenario in which this is not feasible, distribute team members to other teams to be a support for them in making their prototypes more efficient. Alternatively, at teacher discretion, move students on to the Justification portion of the lesson.

- If after the third test the final prototype is still unsuccessful, ask students how they would start over. These challenges are meant to have students build on what they originally designed. If the design proved to be unsuccessful, encourage a reflection/justification on what they would do if they were allowed to start again from scratch.

REFLECTIONS — EXPLAIN & ELABORATE

AFTER TEST TRIAL 1	How long did your prototype hold the weight of the Gingerbread Man? Which team's bridge was able to hold the Gingerbread Man for one minute?
ANALYSIS	What were some of the differences between the different prototypes? What changes will you make to your bridge?
AFTER TEST TRIAL 2	Did your bridge hold the Gingerbread Man longer this time?
ANALYSIS	What changes made other teams' bridges stronger? What changes will you need to make your bridge stronger?
AFTER TEST TRIAL 3	Did your bridge hold the Gingerbread Man longer this time? If you could start again, what would you do differently?

JUSTIFICATION — EVALUATE

ARTS	Create and decorate a gingerbread person using cardboard or cereal boxes and various art supplies.
ELA	Draw, tell, or write a story about a day in the Gingerbread Man's life.

THE THREE MEN HAVE A LEAKY TUB

1 HOUR

TIME FOR COMPLETION

SETTING —THE— STAGE

DESIGN CHALLENGE PURPOSE

Create a floatation device for one of the three men in the tub.

TEACHER DEVELOPMENT

Sinking and **floating** is a traditional kindergarten activity. The standards do not formally address buoyancy for kindergarten. However, this lesson addresses engineering standards and scientific thinking. Refer to the STEAM design process diagram (page 15) for a description of each step.

STUDENT DEVELOPMENT

Students that have never been in a boat or near water may not know what a **floatation** device is. Showing them pictures of various devices can provide them with the background knowledge that they need for this lesson.

When an object is placed in water, it will either sink or float. A flotation device like a life jacket or a life preserver can help a person to float who would otherwise sink. Boats are required to have life jackets on board. Life jackets are flotation devices to keep passengers from sinking if they fall out of the boat.

This is a great lesson for teaching the engineering process to students. Introduce the words **blueprint**, **design**, **engineer**, and **prototype** to your students. Teach them how to collaborate and work as a team. Use the STEAM job cards (page 144) to assign jobs to students to demonstrate the importance of working together.

Note: Visit the website listed on the inside front cover for a link to images of floatation devices.

STANDARDS

SCIENCE	TECHNOLOGY	ENGINEERING	ARTS	MATH	ELA
		K-2-ETS1-1	Creating #1	CCSS.MATH. CONTENT.K.G.A.1	CCSS.ELA-LITERACY.RI.2.1
		K-2-ETS1-2	Creating #2	CCSS.MATH. CONTENT.K.G.A.2	CCSS.ELA-LITERACY.W.2.8
		K-2-ETS1-3	Creating #3		

SCIENCE & ENGINEERING PRACTICES

Asking Questions and Defining Problems: Ask questions based on observations to find more information about the natural and/or designed world(s).

Developing and Using Models: Develop a simple model based on evidence to represent a proposed object or tool.

CROSSCUTTING CONCEPTS

Structure and Function: The shape and stability of structures of natural and designed objects are related to their function(s).

TARGET VOCABULARY

blueprint

design

engineer

float

floatation device

prototype

sink

MATERIALS

- aluminum foil
- clay
- paper
- scissors
- straws
- tape

Testing:

- 1 plastic toy (represents one of the three men)
- tub of water
- stopwatch

LITERACY CONNECTIONS

Rub a Dub Dub (Extended Nursery Rhymes) by Danny and Kim Adlerman

Does It Sink or Float? (What's the Matter?) by Susan Hughes

NOTES

STEAM
— IN —
ACTION

DILEMMA   ENGAGE

Rub-a-dub-dub, the three men have a leaky tub! The butcher, the baker, and the candlestick maker want to take their tub out for a ride in the sea, but the butcher can't swim and they're afraid the tub will spring a leak. Help the three men make a floatation device for the butcher to use in case the tub starts to sink.

MISSION

Build a floatation device that keeps the man (toy) above the water for at least 30 seconds.

BLUEPRINT   EXPLORE

Provide the Individual Blueprint Design sheet, and ask students to sketch a design for a prototype they will describe to the other members of their team. After each team member has presented his or her design, the team as a whole will decide which prototype to construct and then draw it on the Group Blueprint Design sheet. Next, the team will present the design to the teacher for approval and for permission to retrieve their materials and begin construction.

ENGINEERING TASK	TEST TRIAL	ANALYZE	REDESIGN
Each team will build a floatation device that holds the toy above the water for at least 30 seconds.	Teams' floatation device prototypes must keep the toy floating above the water for at least 30 seconds.	Teams will talk about their results and discuss the successful design elements with the class. Teams should be allowed to observe the other designs to gather ideas, reflect, and make changes in order to improve their prototypes.	Teams can use a colored pencil to make adjustments to their original design sketches. Teams will present the changes to the teacher for approval before making changes to the prototypes. Then they can get new supplies to rebuild and retest their prototypes.

HELPFUL TIPS

- After the Test Trial, have teams take a gallery walk to view other teams' designs for possible ideas to assist them in the Analyze and Redesign portions of the engineering design process.

- If teams are successful on the first try, encourage them to make their prototypes even more efficient. If it is a scenario in which this is not feasible, distribute team members to other teams to be a support for them in making their prototypes more efficient. Alternatively, at teacher discretion, move students on to the Justification portion of the lesson.

- If after the third test the final prototype is still unsuccessful, ask students how they would start over. These challenges are meant to have students build on what they originally designed. If the design proved to be unsuccessful, encourage a reflection/justification on what they would do if they were allowed to start again from scratch.

REFLECTIONS — EXPLAIN & ELABORATE

AFTER TEST TRIAL 1	Did your prototype float? What materials did you use?
ANALYSIS	What was the shape of your prototype? Can you change the shape or materials you used to help the prototype float better?
AFTER TEST TRIAL 2	Did your prototype float? If not, can you change something to make it float? If it did float, can you make another floatation device in a different shape or using a different material?
ANALYSIS	Do you need to change part of your prototype to make it float? If your second floatation device was able to float, make a third one using a different shape or different materials.
AFTER TEST TRIAL 3	How many floatation devices did you build?

JUSTIFICATION — EVALUATE

ARTS	Create a poster for your floatation device.
MATH	Describe and name the shapes and materials you used to build your floatation device(s).
ELA	Write an additional verse to the nursery rhyme to show that the three men took your floatation device with them in their tub.

HOME FOR A WILD THING

STEAM

SETTING —THE— STAGE

DESIGN CHALLENGE PURPOSE

Create a shoebox habitat for a "wild thing" and include the resources it would need to survive.

TEACHER DEVELOPMENT

All living things need water, whether they are plants or animals. Plants produce their own food in a process called **photosynthesis**. It begins with the sun. Light from the sun is absorbed by cells in the plant's leaves. Plants use this energy to change water, carbon dioxide, and minerals into food. Animals eat plants and absorb the energy the plants received from the sun. Sometimes animals eat other animals to obtain the energy they received by eating plants.

STUDENT DEVELOPMENT

Students need to understand that plants and animals need water to survive. Plants must have light to make their own food. Animals must have plant or animal food sources to survive.

Lesson Idea: Take students on a nature walk around the school to observe and collect items such as twigs, leaves, and rocks to add to their shoebox habitats. Limit the number of real objects to no more than two of each kind.

STANDARDS

SCIENCE	TECHNOLOGY	ENGINEERING	ARTS	MATH	ELA
K-LS1-1		K-2-ETS1-1	Creating #1	CCSS.MATH. CONTENT.K.CC.A.3	CCSS.ELA-LITERACY.W.K.2
		K-2-ETS1-2	Creating #2		
		K-2-ETS1-3	Creating #3		

SCIENCE & ENGINEERING PRACTICES

Analyzing and Interpreting Data: Use observations (firsthand or from media) to describe patterns in the natural world in order to answer scientific questions.

CROSSCUTTING CONCEPTS

Patterns: Patterns in the natural and human-designed world can be observed and used as evidence.

TARGET VOCABULARY

animal

food

habitat

plant

water

MATERIALS

- glue
- shoebox
- construction paper
- tissue paper
- yarn
- leaves, sticks, and rocks (collected on nature walk)
- sand
- any other materials you think are necessary
- data sheet (page 135)

LITERACY CONNECTIONS

Where the Wild Things Are by Maurice Sendak

Uno's Garden by Graeme Base

NOTES

STEAM —IN— ACTION

DILEMMA ENGAGE

Note: Read aloud, *Where the Wild Things Are* by Maurice Sendak before introducing the dilemma.

Max has brought a "wild thing" home with him. He needs to make his new friend a place to live before his mother finds out. Can you help?

MISSION

Build a habitat for a "wild thing." It must have 10 trees, 7 plants, 2 water sources, and 4 food sources.

BLUEPRINT EXPLORE

Provide the Individual Blueprint Design sheet, and ask students to sketch a design for a prototype they will describe to the other members of their team. After each team member has presented his or her design, the team as a whole will decide which prototype to construct and then draw it on the Group Blueprint Design sheet. Next, the team will present the design to the teacher for approval and for permission to retrieve their materials and begin construction.

ENGINEERING TASK

Create a habitat for a "wild thing". It must include 10 trees, 7 plants (not trees), 4 sources of food, and 2 sources of water. Teams should count out and collect the items themselves in order to reinforce counting skills.

Note: If the "wild thing" is an herbivore or omnivore, the four food sources should be in addition to the plants.

TEST TRIAL

Assign each team a partner team. Then have partner teams evaluate each other's habitats using the data sheet.

Teams should count and record the number of trees, plants, food sources, and water sources in their partner team's habitat. They should return the completed data sheet to their partner team so the partner team knows what to change during the redesign stage.

ANALYZE

Teams will use the completed data sheet to ensure that they have the correct number of trees, plants, food sources, and water sources.

REDESIGN

Teams will use the completed data sheet to determine what they need to add to their designs to meet the requirements.

HELPFUL TIPS

- After the Test Trial, have teams take a gallery walk to view other teams' designs for possible ideas to assist them in the Analyze and Redesign portions of the engineering design process.

- If teams are successful on the first try, encourage them to make their prototypes even more efficient. If it is a scenario in which this is not feasible, distribute team members to other teams to be a support for them in making their prototypes more efficient. Alternatively, at teacher discretion, move students on to the Justification portion of the lesson.

- If after the third test the final prototype is still unsuccessful, ask students how they would start over. These challenges are meant to have students build on what they originally designed. If the design proved to be unsuccessful, encourage a reflection/justification on what they would do if they were allowed to start again from scratch.

REFLECTIONS EXPLAIN & ELABORATE

AFTER TEST TRIAL 1	Use the first section of the data sheet to evaluate and count the number of trees, plants, food sources, and water sources in your partner team's habitat. Return the completed data sheet to your partner team.
ANALYSIS	Compare the information in the first section of your data sheet to your habitat. What changes do you need to make?
AFTER TEST TRIAL 2	Look at your partner team's habitat. Use the second section on your partner team's data sheet to count the number of trees, plants, food sources, and water sources in their habitat. Return the completed data sheet to your partner team.
ANALYSIS	Compare the information in the second section of your data sheet to your habitat. What changes do you need to make?
AFTER TEST TRIAL 3	Instead of recording observations about your partner team's habitat, this time use the third section of your data sheet to make observations about your own team's habitat. Does your team's habitat have all of the trees, plants, food sources, and water sources it needs? Fill out the bottom section of your data sheet.

JUSTIFICATION EVALUATE

ARTS	Use art materials to create a "wild thing" that could live in your team's habitat.
MATH	Display all of the finished habitats in a section of the classroom. Invite students to count and record the total number of trees, plants, food sources, and water sources in each habitat. Then as a whole group, repeat this count and record the numbers on a class chart. Compare the two recorded totals to check for accuracy.

HUNGRY PETS

2-3 HOURS

TIME FOR COMPLETION

S t E A M

SETTING
— THE —
STAGE

DESIGN CHALLENGE PURPOSE
Build an automatic pet feeder.

TEACHER DEVELOPMENT

All living things need water, whether they are **plants** or **animals**. Plants produce their own food in a process called **photosynthesis**. It begins with the sun. Light from the sun is absorbed by cells in the plant's leaves. Plants use this energy to change water, carbon dioxide, and minerals into food. Animals eat plants and absorb the energy from the plants. Sometimes animals eat other animals for the same reason.

STUDENT DEVELOPMENT

Talk with students about living things. Be sure they know that living things need air, food and water.

Lesson Idea: Hold a pet picture show-and-tell! Have students bring in pictures of their pets. They should be prepared to talk about what kind of food their pets eat and how often they are fed.

STANDARDS

SCIENCE	TECHNOLOGY	ENGINEERING	ARTS	MATH	ELA
K-LS1-1		K-2-ETS1-1	Creating #1	CCSS.MATH. CONTENT.K.CC.B.5	CCSS.ELA-LITERACY.SL.K.1
		K-2-ETS1-2	Creating #2		CCSS.ELA-LITERACY.W.K.2
		K-2-ETS1-3	Creating #3		

SCIENCE & ENGINEERING PRACTICES

Analyzing and Interpreting Data: Use observations (firsthand or from media) to describe patterns in the natural world in order to answer scientific questions.

CROSSCUTTING CONCEPTS

Patterns: Patterns in the natural and human-designed world can be observed and used as evidence.

TARGET VOCABULARY

animal

automatic

food

living thing

pet

MATERIALS

- paper towel tubes
- plastic water bottles with the bottoms cut off
- plastic water bottles with the tops cut off
- plastic cups
- Styrofoam cups
- tape
- scissors
- 2 cups of dry cereal
- small spoon

LITERACY CONNECTIONS

Everything Pets by James Spears

What Pet Should I Get? by Dr. Seuss

NOTES

STEAM —IN— ACTION

DILEMMA — ENGAGE

Marvin loves animals! But animals need a lot of care. He needs to feed his rabbit, his turtle, his cat, and his dog. He must feed his pets before leaving for school. It takes a long time to feed them because they each eat a different type of food. Help Marvin create an automatic feeder prototype to use as a model for building a feeder for each of his pets so he can make it to school on time.

Note: Visit the website listed on the inside front cover for a link to an image of an automatic pet feeder.

MISSION

Create an automatic pet feeder. It must hold two cups of dry food and be easy for an animal (plastic spoon) to get the food out.

BLUEPRINT — EXPLORE

Provide the Individual Blueprint Design sheet, and ask students to sketch a design for a prototype they will describe to the other members of their team. After each team member has presented his or her design, the team as a whole will decide which prototype to construct and then draw it on the Group Blueprint Design sheet. Next, the team will present the design to the teacher for approval and for permission to retrieve their materials and begin construction.

ENGINEERING TASK	TEST TRIAL	ANALYZE	REDESIGN
Each team will build an automatic pet feeder. The feeder must hold at least two cups of dry food (cereal).	Each team will pour exactly two cups of food into its automatic pet feeder prototype. Team members will use a spoon to represent the animal eating. They will remove the food from the opening in the feeder using the spoon, and continue until all of the food is removed or until they cannot reach the food with the spoon. Teams will dump out any remaining food and count the number of pieces left.	Teams will determine if they could easily add and remove the dry food (cereal) from their prototypes. Teams should be allowed to observe the other designs to gather ideas, reflect, and make changes in order to improve their prototypes.	Teams can use a colored pencil to make adjustments to their original design sketches. Teams will present the changes to the teacher for approval before making changes to the prototypes. Then they can get new supplies to rebuild and retest their prototypes.

HELPFUL TIPS

- After the Test Trial, have teams take a gallery walk to view other teams' designs for possible ideas to assist them in the Analyze and Redesign portions of the engineering design process.

- If teams are successful on the first try, encourage them to make their prototypes even more efficient. If it is a scenario in which this is not feasible, distribute team members to other teams to be a support for them in making their prototypes more efficient. Alternatively, at teacher discretion, move students on to the Justification portion of the lesson.

- If after the third test the final prototype is still unsuccessful, ask students how they would start over. These challenges are meant to have students build on what they originally designed. If the design proved to be unsuccessful, encourage a reflection/justification on what they would do if they were allowed to start again from scratch.

REFLECTIONS — **E**XPLAIN & **E**LABORATE

AFTER TEST TRIAL 1	Did your automatic feeder prototype hold two cups of dry food? Was it easy for you to get the food out? How many pieces of food were left inside your feeder?
ANALYSIS	What will you change to make your prototype work better? Explain.
AFTER TEST TRIAL 2	Were the changes you made helpful? How many pieces of food were left inside your feeder?
ANALYSIS	What will you change to make your prototype work better? Explain.
AFTER TEST TRIAL 3	Were the changes you made helpful? How many pieces of food were left inside your feeder? What did the successful prototypes have in common?

JUSTIFICATION — **E**VALUATE

ARTS	Create a poster advertising your automatic pet feeder.
ELA	Write three sentences describing your automatic pet feeder.

JACK NEEDS A BEANSTALK

1-2 HOURS
TIME FOR COMPLETION
ADDITIONAL 2-3 WEEKS FOR GROWING AND OBSERVATION

S t e A M

SETTING
—THE—
STAGE

DESIGN CHALLENGE PURPOSE
Grow the tallest "beanstalk" for Jack.

TEACHER DEVELOPMENT

All living things need water, whether they are **plants** or **animals**. Plants produce their own food in a process called **photosynthesis**. It begins with the sun. Light from the sun is absorbed by cells in the plant's leaves. Plants use this energy to change water, carbon dioxide, and minerals into food.

S t e A M

STUDENT DEVELOPMENT

Review the vocabulary with students prior to the challenge. Remind students that plants need light and water to live. Discuss what other things they think will help their beanstalks grow.

Lesson Idea: Have students germinate a lima bean seed. Ahead of time, soak the lima bean seeds for approximately 8 hours. You can prepare one seed per student or one seed per group. Have students wrap the seed in a wet paper towel, place the wrapped seed inside a plastic bag, and seal it. Then tape the bag to a sunny window. Check the seed every day to see if it has sprouted. The process usually takes from 4 to 7 days. Students may need to periodically spray the paper towel with water if it dries out.

Note: If using these seeds for the challenge, be sure to germinate several extra seeds in case of mishaps.

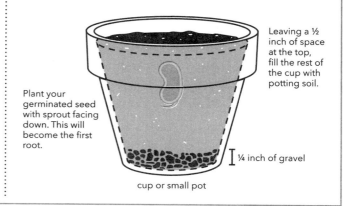

Leaving a ½ inch of space at the top, fill the rest of the cup with potting soil.

Plant your germinated seed with sprout facing down. This will become the first root.

¼ inch of gravel

cup or small pot

STANDARDS

SCIENCE	TECHNOLOGY	ENGINEERING	ARTS	MATH	ELA
K-LS1-1			Creating #1	CCSS.MATH.CONTENT.K.MD.A.2	CCSS.ELA-LITERACY.W.K.3
			Creating #2		
			Creating #3		

SCIENCE & ENGINEERING PRACTICES

Analyzing and Interpreting Data: Use observations (firsthand or from media) to describe patterns in the natural world in order to answer scientific questions.

CROSSCUTTING CONCEPTS

Patterns: Patterns in the natural and human-designed world can be observed and used as evidence.

TARGET VOCABULARY

light

plant

seed

sun

water

MATERIALS

- germinated lima bean seeds (see student development for directions)
- plastic cups or small pots
- soil
- gravel
- skewers
- string
- plastic spoons
- watering schedule (page 136)
- classroom map (page 137)
- observation sheet (page 138)

LITERACY CONNECTIONS

Jack and the Beanstalk by Steven Kellogg

Trust Me, Jack's Beanstalk Stinks!: The Story of Jack and the Beanstalk as Told by the Giant by Eric Braun and Cristian Bernardini

NOTES

STEAM
—IN—
ACTION

DILEMMA ENGAGE

Jack needs a new beanstalk because he chopped down the first one. His special hen that lays golden eggs has flown back up to the city of giants in the clouds, and he needs to get her back. He knows plants need some important things to survive, but he just can't remember what they are.

Use what you know about what plants need, and grow a new beanstalk for Jack.

MISSION

Grow the tallest beanstalk you can. Choose your watering schedule and a spot on the plant placement map that you think will help your plant grow.

BLUEPRINT EXPLORE

Provide the Individual Blueprint Design Sheet, and ask students to sketch or list one item they will need to grow their beanstalk. Once sketches are done, have each group decide which sketch they will use for growing their beanstalk, which watering schedule they will follow, and where they will place the beanstalk in the classroom. Before providing materials, have teams complete the Group Blueprint Design Sheet and then write or verbalize why they chose the design they chose and why they feel that the other designs would not work as well.

ENGINEERING TASK	TEST TRIAL	ANALYZE	REDESIGN
Each team will try to grow the tallest beanstalk. Guide teams through the process of planting their seeds. Refer to the diagram in student development. Teams must choose a watering schedule and a spot on the plant placement map. Check the height and record observations on the beanstalk observation sheet every three to five days.	Once a seed is planted, the team will place it in the location selected on the placement map. The team will water the plant on the first day and then continue following the watering schedule it selected.	Teams will observe and record the growth of their plants. They should record the height on their observation sheets. Teams should be allowed to observe the other plants to compare the growth progress and help them decide whether or not to change their watering plan or the location of their plant in the classroom.	Teams will use the observation sheet to determine what changes they need to make to their plan. Teams should use colored pencil to make changes to their watering schedule and/or to location of their plant in the classroom.

HELPFUL TIPS

- After the Test Trial, have teams take a gallery walk to view other teams' designs for possible ideas to assist them in the Analyze and Redesign portions of the engineering design process.

- If teams are successful on the first try, encourage them to make their prototypes even more efficient. If it is a scenario in which this is not feasible, distribute team members to other teams to be a support for them in making their prototypes more efficient. Alternatively, at teacher discretion, move students on to the Justification portion of the lesson.

- If after the third test the final prototype is still unsuccessful, ask students how they would start over. These challenges are meant to have students build on what they originally designed. If the design proved to be unsuccessful, encourage a reflection/justification on what they would do if they were allowed to start again from scratch.

REFLECTIONS — EXPLAIN & ELABORATE

AFTER TEST TRIAL 1	Has your lima bean grown? Is the soil wet or dry? How does your plant's height compare to the height of the other teams' plants? Is it taller than anyone else's plant? Is it shorter than anyone else's plant? How tall is it compared to the chart on your observation sheet?
ANALYSIS	Will you move your plant to a different spot in the classroom? Will you change the watering schedule for your plant? Explain.
AFTER TEST TRIAL 2	What observations can you make about your plant? Did the changes you made make a difference in how much it has grown? Explain.
ANALYSIS	Will you move your plant to a different spot in the classroom? Will you change the watering schedule for your plant? Explain.
AFTER TEST TRIAL 3	Has your lima bean grown? Is the soil wet or dry? How does your plant's height compare to the height of the other teams' plants? Is it taller than anyone else's plant? Is it shorter than anyone else's plant? How tall is it compared to the chart on your observation sheet?

JUSTIFICATION — EVALUATE

ELA/ARTS	Write, tell, or draw a story about how Jack used your beanstalk to climb back up to the city of giants to get his special hen and bring her back home.

MUSEUM MIX-UP

1 HOUR
TIME FOR COMPLETION

S t e A m

SETTING
—THE—
STAGE

DESIGN CHALLENGE PURPOSE

Help the museum create accurate animal displays.

TEACHER DEVELOPMENT

A museum that educates the public about **animals** and their **habitats** is known as a natural history museum or science museum. Many of your students may have never visited this type of museum. They will need to know that the museum researches the animals, their habitat, and the food the animal eats so that it can accurately create the display and educate the museum visitors.

STUDENT DEVELOPMENT

Students will need to understand how museums provide displays for people to view and learn about animals. Students will need to research their given animal so that they can complete their diorama accurately. Pre-teaching the animals and the foods they eat and the habitat where they live will help students recall the information that they will need to complete this task.

Note: Visit the website listed on the inside front cover for a link to more information about animals and their habitats.

STANDARDS

SCIENCE	TECHNOLOGY	ENGINEERING	ARTS	MATH	ELA
K-ESS3-1			Creating #1		CCSS.ELA-LITERACY.SL.K.1
K-LS1-1			Creating #2		CCSS.ELA-LITERACY.W.K.3
			Creating #3		

SCIENCE & ENGINEERING PRACTICES

Developing and Using Models: Use a model to represent relationships in the natural world.

Analyzing and Interpreting Data: Use observations (firsthand or from media) to describe patterns in the natural world in order to answer scientific questions.

CROSSCUTTING CONCEPTS

Systems and System Models: Systems in the natural and designed world have parts that work together.

Patterns: Patterns in the natural and human-designed world can be observed and used as evidence.

TARGET VOCABULARY

animal

food

food supply

habitat

museum

MATERIALS

- white construction paper
- crayons
- animal cards (page 139)
- certificate (page 140)

LITERACY CONNECTIONS

Pond Animals by Francine Galko

Forest Animals by Francine Galko

Rain Forest Animals by Francine Galko

Mountain Animals by Francine Galko

NOTES

DILEMMA — ENGAGE

Dr. Docent, the director of the local natural history museum, has a problem! Someone broke into the museum and mixed up some of the animal displays. They moved the animals and what they eat to different habitat displays. Can you help Dr. Docent design a new display? The teams that complete this challenge will receive a certificate from the museum.

MISSION

Create a display that shows an animal in its correct habitat and with its correct food.

BLUEPRINT — EXPLORE

Provide the Individual Blueprint Design sheet, and ask students to sketch a design for a prototype they will describe to the other members of their team. After each team member has presented his or her design, the team as a whole will decide which prototype to construct and then draw it on the Group Blueprint Design sheet. Next, the team will present the design to the teacher for approval and for permission to retrieve their materials and begin construction.

ENGINEERING TASK **TEST TRIAL** **ANALYZE** **REDESIGN**

Each team will use the cards to match an animal to what it needs to survive in its habitat. The team then uses these cards to create the habitat on a mini poster.

Note: Suggested cards are included (page 137). However, you can create additional cards with information about other animals.

Extension idea: Create a natural history museum in your classroom. Display team mini posters and invite parents or other classes to visit. Have teams explain their posters to visitors.

Each team will select one animal card and then try to select the correct food and habitat cards for this animal. The team will place these cards on top of the construction paper mini poster so the teacher can check for accuracy.

Teams will repeat this process with new cards for each test trial until after the final test trial when they will glue the final three cards to the paper and add more details to the mini poster habitat.

Each team will determine if its selected animal eats the food listed on the food card and lives in the habitat listed on the habitat card.

Team mini posters should show the correct food and the correct habitat for the animal selected. If teams have chosen any incorrect cards, they must replace them with the correct cards.

 # HELPFUL TIPS

- After the Test Trial, have teams take a gallery walk to view other teams' designs for possible ideas to assist them in the Analyze and Redesign portions of the engineering design process.

- If teams are successful on the first try, encourage them to make their prototypes even more efficient. If it is a scenario in which this is not feasible, distribute team members to other teams to be a support for them in making their prototypes more efficient. Alternatively, at teacher discretion, move students on to the Justification portion of the lesson.

- If after the third test the final prototype is still unsuccessful, ask students how they would start over. These challenges are meant to have students build on what they originally designed. If the design proved to be unsuccessful, encourage a reflection/justification on what they would do if they were allowed to start again from scratch.

REFLECTIONS EXPLAIN & ELABORATE

AFTER TEST TRIAL 1	Check with your teacher. Did you match the correct animal with its food and habitat?
ANALYSIS	Do you need to make a change? If you got it right, can you try to match another animal with its food and habitat?
AFTER TEST TRIAL 2	Check with your teacher. Did you match the next animal correctly with its food and habitat?
ANALYSIS	Do you need to make a change? If you got it right, can you try to match another animal with its food and habitat?
AFTER TEST TRIAL 3	Did you match the third animal to the correct food and habitat?

JUSTIFICATION EVALUATE

ARTS	Design a sign for your mini poster that tells one fact about the animal.
ELA	Draw, tell, or write a story about an animal in its habitat.

A CHAIR FOR GOLDILOCKS

2-3 HOURS

TIME FOR COMPLETION

SETTING —THE— STAGE

DESIGN CHALLENGE PURPOSE

Design and construct a chair to hold the weight of Goldilocks (a stuffed animal).

TEACHER DEVELOPMENT

For this lesson, students will need to understand a few concepts. A **force** is a push or pull. A **push** or **pull** can cause **motion**. An object moves in the direction of a push or pull. Pushes and pulls can speed up, slow down, or change the direction of an object in motion. In addition, the size, weight, and shape of an object can affect its motion.

STUDENT DEVELOPMENT

Discuss vocabulary words (**push**, **pull**, and **motion**) as well as examples of cause-and-effect relationships with students. Some examples of cause-and-effect relationships include *I had a question, so I raised my hand. It was raining, so I opened up my umbrella. I was thirsty, so I got a drink of water.* Ask students to think about questions such as *What does it mean to push something? Give an example of something that can be pushed. What does it mean to pull? Give an example of something you can pull. What happens to objects when they are pushed or pulled?*

Lesson Idea: Lead a discussion about things that are normally pushed and pulled. Start by providing an example for each. A swing is something that is usually pushed. A kite attached to a string is something that is usually pulled.

STANDARDS

SCIENCE	TECHNOLOGY	ENGINEERING	ARTS	MATH	ELA
K-PS2-1		K-2-ETS1-1	Creating #1	MATH. CONTENT.K.MD.A.2	CCSS.ELA-LITERACY.SL.K.1
		K-2-ETS1-2		MATH. CONTENT.K.G.A.1	CCSS.ELA-LITERACY.W.K.3
		K-2-ETS1-3			

SCIENCE & ENGINEERING PRACTICES

Planning and Carrying Out Investigations: With guidance, plan and conduct an investigation in collaboration with peers.

Scientific Investigations Use a Variety of Methods: Scientists use different ways to study the world.

CROSSCUTTING CONCEPTS

Cause and Effect: Simple tests can be designed to gather evidence to support or refute student ideas about causes.

TARGET VOCABULARY

force

motion

pull

push

support

weight

MATERIALS

- tape
- glue
- cardboard pieces
- construction paper
- craft sticks
- stuffed animal
- egg carton cups

LITERACY CONNECTIONS

Goldilocks and the Three Bears by Parragon Books

Goldilocks and the Three Bears by Jan Brett

How Things Move by Don L. Curry

NOTES

STEAM —IN— ACTION

DILEMMA ENGAGE

Goldilocks was tired after she finished eating porridge. She needed somewhere to rest. Goldilocks sat in one chair, but it felt too big. She sat in another chair, but it felt too small. She sat in one more chair, and it felt just right until…it broke! Can you help Goldilocks build a chair that won't break when she sits on it?

MISSION

Build a chair that is just the right size for Goldilocks. The chair must hold her without breaking. It must have legs, a seat, and a back.

BLUEPRINT EXPLORE

Provide the Individual Blueprint Design sheet, and ask students to sketch a design for a prototype they will describe to the other members of their team. After each team member has presented his or her design, the team as a whole will decide which prototype to construct and then draw it on the Group Blueprint Design sheet. Next, the team will present the design to the teacher for approval and for permission to retrieve their materials and begin construction.

ENGINEERING TASK   **TEST TRIAL**   **ANALYZE** **REDESIGN**

ENGINEERING TASK	TEST TRIAL	ANALYZE	REDESIGN
Each team will build a chair that can hold the weight of Goldilocks (a stuffed animal).	Teams will test their prototypes by putting Goldilocks (the stuffed animal) on the chair and observing whether or not the chair can hold the weight. Ensure that students make observations about what happens during each team's trial. They should talk about what parts of each chair seem to help it hold up the stuffed animal.	Teams will talk about their results and discuss the successful design elements with the class. Teams should be allowed to observe the other designs to gather ideas, reflect, and make changes in order to improve their prototypes.	Teams can use a colored pencil to make adjustments to their original design sketches. Teams will present the changes to the teacher for approval before making changes to the prototypes. Then they can get new supplies to rebuild and retest their prototypes.

HELPFUL TIPS

- After the Test Trial, have teams take a gallery walk to view other teams' designs for possible ideas to assist them in the Analyze and Redesign portions of the engineering design process.

- If teams are successful on the first try, encourage them to make their prototypes even more efficient. If it is a scenario in which this is not feasible, distribute team members to other teams to be a support for them in making their prototypes more efficient. Alternatively, at teacher discretion, move students on to the Justification portion of the lesson.

- If after the third test the final prototype is still unsuccessful, ask students how they would start over. These challenges are meant to have students build on what they originally designed. If the design proved to be unsuccessful, encourage a reflection/justification on what they would do if they were allowed to start again from scratch.

STEAM Design Challenges Gr. K © 2017 Creative Teaching Press

REFLECTIONS — EXPLAIN & ELABORATE

AFTER TEST TRIAL 1	Which team's chair could hold Goldilocks without breaking? Did you notice any differences between the chairs? What were they?
ANALYSIS	If you could change the design of your chair, what would you do differently?
AFTER TEST TRIAL 2	Did your chair hold the weight of Goldilocks? Were there any other teams that built chairs that could hold the weight of Goldilocks?
ANALYSIS	What materials seemed to work the best?
AFTER TEST TRIAL 3	What would you change about your design so your chair could hold more weight?

JUSTIFICATION — EVALUATE

ELA/ARTS

Note: Students will need copies of the comic strip on page 141.

Draw a comic strip retelling the story of "Goldilocks and the Three Bears."

PROTECT HUMPTY

S t E a M

SETTING
— THE —
STAGE

DESIGN CHALLENGE PURPOSE

Create a protective device for a car passenger.

TEACHER DEVELOPMENT

Newton's third law is important in this challenge: for every action, there is an equal and opposite reaction. Students will not understand this law yet. However, discussing car rides and what happens when the car stops suddenly will help them understand that when they are riding in a car, their body wants to keep moving forward even after the brake is applied.

You may want to demonstrate the importance of passenger safety by releasing a toy car with an unrestrained egg on board down a ramp so that it hits a wall.

STUDENT DEVELOPMENT

Students will need to understand the concept of motion (pull and push). It is also helpful to discuss how students feel when they are riding in a car and the driver stops quickly.

Discussion ideas: Ask students to demonstrate in their seats what happens when their mom or dad has to suddenly apply the breaks when they're riding in a car. Also ask them to demonstrate what happens when they go down a slide fast and get to the bottom.

Restraints and safety devices are important to talk about beforehand as this discussion gives small children ideas about seat belts and how they work.

STANDARDS

SCIENCE	TECHNOLOGY	ENGINEERING	ARTS	MATH	ELA
K-PS2-2		K-2-ETS1-3		CCSS.MATH.CONTENT.K.MD.A.1	CCSS.ELA-LITERACY.W.K.2

SCIENCE & ENGINEERING PRACTICES

Analyzing and Interpreting Data: Analyze data from tests of an object or tool to determine if it works as intended.

CROSSCUTTING CONCEPTS

Cause and Effect: Simple tests can be designed to gather evidence to support or refute student ideas about causes.

TARGET VOCABULARY

protection

pull

push

restraint

MATERIALS

- cotton
- plastic eggs (filled with liquid soap)
- yarn
- string
- rubber bands
- toy car (large enough to fit an egg in the seat)
- ramp (book propped up)
- autograph (page 142)

LITERACY CONNECTIONS

Humpty Dumpty by Josie Stewart and Lynn Salem

My Trusty Car Seat: Buckling Up for Safety by Stan Berenstain and Jan Berenstain

NOTES

DILEMMA ENGAGE

After Humpty Dumpty's fall, his friend Rowdy, the race car driver, challenged him to a car race. Humpty was a little worried because the car that Rowdy loaned him was not safe. There was no safety device inside the car! Humpty was afraid that if he stopped suddenly or hit something, he might fall out. He decided to make the car safer by adding something to keep him inside the car in case of an accident. Help Humpty build a safety device. Teams that successfully complete this challenge will earn a checkered flag signed by Humpty Dumpty.

MISSION

Design a safety device that keeps Humpty safe inside the car when it hits a wall.

BLUEPRINT EXPLORE

Provide the Individual Blueprint Design sheet, and ask students to sketch a design for a prototype they will describe to the other members of their team. After each team member has presented his or her design, the team as a whole will decide which prototype to construct and then draw it on the Group Blueprint Design sheet. Next, the team will present the design to the teacher for approval and for permission to retrieve their materials and begin construction.

ENGINEERING TASK	TEST TRIAL	ANALYZE	REDESIGN
Each team will build a restraint for Humpty so he does not fall out of the car or get injured when the car hits a wall. *Note:* The teacher will fill the eggs with liquid soap prior to the start of the challenge.	Each team will secure its egg to the seat of the toy car with its choice of an item from the materials list. The car will travel down a ramp and hit a wall. Teams observe the test to see if the egg remains in its seat and stays in one piece.	Teams will talk about their results and discuss the successful design elements with the class. Teams should be allowed to observe the other designs to gather ideas, reflect, and make changes in order to improve their prototypes.	Teams can use a colored pencil to make adjustments to their original design sketches. Teams will present the changes to the teacher for approval before making changes to the prototypes. Then they can get new supplies to rebuild and retest their prototypes.

HELPFUL TIPS

- After the Test Trial, have teams take a gallery walk to view other teams' designs for possible ideas to assist them in the Analyze and Redesign portions of the engineering design process.

- If teams are successful on the first try, encourage them to make their prototypes even more efficient. If it is a scenario in which this is not feasible, distribute team members to other teams to be a support for them in making their prototypes more efficient. Alternatively, at teacher discretion, move students on to the Justification portion of the lesson.

- If after the third test the final prototype is still unsuccessful, ask students how they would start over. These challenges are meant to have students build on what they originally designed. If the design proved to be unsuccessful, encourage a reflection/justification on what they would do if they were allowed to start again from scratch.

REFLECTIONS EXPLAIN & ELABORATE

AFTER TEST TRIAL 1	Was Humpty still in one piece after hitting the wall? Which material did you use to keep Humpty in his seat?
ANALYSIS	Do you want to keep using the same material to keep Humpty in his seat or do you want to try a different material?
AFTER TEST TRIAL 2	Do you want to keep using the same material to keep Humpty in his seat? Which material did you use to keep Humpty safe?
ANALYSIS	Do you want to keep using the same material or do you want to change it?
AFTER TEST TRIAL 3	Was Humpty still in one piece after hitting the wall? Which material worked the best to keep Humpty safe? Why do you think that this material worked the best?

JUSTIFICATION EVALUATE

ELA	Create a safety poster about the importance of wearing seat belts.

RESCUE RAPUNZEL

2-3 HOURS

TIME FOR COMPLETION

SETTING —THE— STAGE

DESIGN CHALLENGE PURPOSE

Design a pulley to help Rapunzel escape from her tower.

TEACHER DEVELOPMENT

A **force** makes an object move or stop moving. When we **push** something, we are moving it away from ourselves. When we **pull** something, we are moving it closer to ourselves. The greater the strength used in pushing or pulling, the greater the **motion** caused. A **pulley** is a simple machine that can use both pushes and pulls to create motion.

STUDENT DEVELOPMENT

Students in kindergarten have background knowledge about how to push and pull toys to get them to move. They know that different strengths of pushes and pulls will get them different results in movement. Students may need to see some images of pulleys before beginning this challenge.

Lesson Idea: Have students play or sing a movement song such as "The Hokey Pokey." Discuss how they can push their body parts forward and then pull them back toward their body. Have students brainstorm other objects in the classroom that they can use to demonstrate pushing and pulling. Ask them what needs to be done in order to move these items.

Note: Visit the website listed on the inside front cover for a link to images of pulleys.

STANDARDS

SCIENCE	TECHNOLOGY	ENGINEERING	ARTS	MATH	ELA/LITERACY
K-PS2-1		K-2-ETS1-1	Creating #1		CCSS.ELA-LITERACY.SL.K.1
K-PS2-2		K-2-ETS1-2	Creating #2		CCSS.ELA-LITERACY.W.K.3
		K-2-ETS1-3	Creating #3		

SCIENCE & ENGINEERING PRACTICES

Planning and Carrying Out Investigations: With guidance, plan and conduct an investigation in collaboration with peers.

Analyzing and Interpreting Data: Analyze data from tests of an object or tool to determine if it works as intended.

CROSSCUTTING CONCEPTS

Cause and Effect: Simple tests can be designed to gather evidence to support or refute student ideas about causes.

TARGET VOCABULARY

force

motion

pull

pulley

push

MATERIALS

- string
- paper clips
- paper cups
- tape
- toilet paper tubes
- pencils
- small toy (Rapunzel)

LITERACY CONNECTIONS

Tangled: The Story of Rapunzel
by Disney Book Group

Motion: Push and Pull, Fast and Slow
by Darlene R. Stille

Give It a Push! Give It a Pull!
by Jennifer Boothroyd

NOTES

STEAM
—IN—
ACTION

DILEMMA — ENGAGE

Poor Rapunzel is stranded alone in her tower with no way to escape. The tower has no stairs or door and only one window at the tippy top. She spends her days singing and daydreaming, and waiting for the prince to come and visit. The prince usually climbs up Rapunzel's hair, but he wants to rescue her this time. How will she ever get to the bottom of the tower so that they can live happily ever after?!

Help Rapunzel escape the tower by building a pulley to safely lower her to the ground.

MISSION

Design a pulley to help safely lower Rapunzel down from her tower.

BLUEPRINT — EXPLORE

Provide the Individual Blueprint Design sheet, and ask students to sketch a design for a prototype they will describe to the other members of their team. After each team member has presented his or her design, the team as a whole will decide which prototype to construct and then draw it on the Group Blueprint Design sheet. Next, the team will present the design to the teacher for approval and for permission to retrieve their materials and begin construction.

ENGINEERING TASK

Each team will construct a pulley to safely lower Rapunzel from her tower.

TEST TRIAL

Each team will attach its pulley to a desk or chair, connect the other end to the floor, and then attempt to lower Rapunzel (small toy) without dropping her.

ANALYZE

Teams will talk about their results and discuss the successful design elements with the class.

Teams should be allowed to observe the other designs to gather ideas, reflect, and make changes in order to improve their prototypes.

REDESIGN

Teams can use a colored pencil to make adjustments to their original design sketches. Teams will present the changes to the teacher for approval before making changes to the prototypes. Then they can get new supplies to rebuild and retest their prototypes.

HELPFUL TIPS

- After the Test Trial, have teams take a gallery walk to view other teams' designs for possible ideas to assist them in the Analyze and Redesign portions of the engineering design process.

- If teams are successful on the first try, encourage them to make their prototypes even more efficient. If it is a scenario in which this is not feasible, distribute team members to other teams to be a support for them in making their prototypes more efficient. Alternatively, at teacher discretion, move students on to the Justification portion of the lesson.

- If after the third test the final prototype is still unsuccessful, ask students how they would start over. These challenges are meant to have students build on what they originally designed. If the design proved to be unsuccessful, encourage a reflection/justification on what they would do if they were allowed to start again from scratch.

S t **E** **A** m

REFLECTIONS — EXPLAIN & ELABORATE

AFTER TEST TRIAL 1	Were you able to move your pulley up and down? Was Rapunzel lowered safely without falling?
ANALYSIS	What could you change to improve your prototype?
AFTER TEST TRIAL 2	Were you able to safely lower Rapunzel? Did your pulley work better this time around?
ANALYSIS	What were some similarities and differences between your design and the designs of other teams?
AFTER TEST TRIAL 3	Were the changes you made to your design helpful? Why or why not?

JUSTIFICATION — EVALUATE

ARTS	Create a poster advertising your pulley and present it to the class.
ELA	Draw, tell, or write a story about a day in Rapunzel's life. Include details about how she used your pulley to escape from the tower.

SLEDS ON THE SAND

2-3 HOURS

TIME FOR COMPLETION

SETTING —THE— STAGE

DESIGN CHALLENGE PURPOSE

Build a sled for moving materials down a sandy surface.

TEACHER DEVELOPMENT

A **force** makes an object move or stop moving. When we **push** something, we are moving it away from ourselves. When we **pull** something, we are moving it closer to ourselves. The greater the strength used in pushing or pulling, the greater the **motion** caused. A ramp is a simple machine that can use both pushes and pulls to increase the speed of an object. A **ramp** can also be used to decrease the amount of force needed to move an object.

STUDENT DEVELOPMENT

For this activity, students will need to understand that when they push or pull an object, it changes position or moves. Ensure students are familiar with the vocabulary (**force**, **push**, **pull**, **motion**, **ramp**).

Lesson Idea: Familiarize students with the effect the height of a ramp has on the speed of an object traveling down the ramp. Have students prop up one end of a book to create a ramp. Then have them release a ping-pong ball at the top of the ramp. Next, have students adjust the height of the ramp (either higher or lower) and release the ping-pong ball again, taking note of the difference in how fast the ball traveled. Discuss students' observations.

STANDARDS

SCIENCE	TECHNOLOGY	ENGINEERING	ARTS	MATH	ELA
K-PS2-2		K-2-ETS1-1	Creating #1		CCSS.ELA-LITERACY.SL.K.1
		K-2-ETS1-2	Creating #2		CCSS.ELA-LITERACY.W.K.3
		K-2-ETS1-3	Creating #3		

SCIENCE & ENGINEERING PRACTICES

Analyzing and Interpreting Data: Analyze data from tests of an object or tool to determine if it works as intended.

STEAM

CROSSCUTTING CONCEPTS

Cause and Effect: Simple tests can be designed to gather evidence to support or refute student ideas about causes.

TARGET VOCABULARY

force

load

motion

pull

push

ramp

LITERACY CONNECTIONS

Ten on the Sled
by Kim Norman

MATERIALS

Sled:
- craft sticks
- straws
- string
- tape
- paper
- cardboard (like cereal boxes)
- empty toilet paper tubes

Load:
- 5 large marshmallows
- 5 toothpicks

Testing:
- 1 aluminum roasting pan or similar large container
- ramp at least 12 in. long
- stopwatch
- sand (optional)

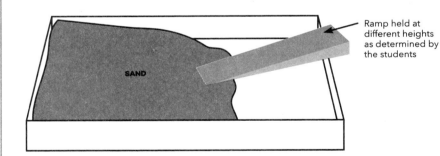

SAND

Ramp held at different heights as determined by the students

NOTES

STEAM
—IN—
ACTION

DILEMMA ENGAGE

Every winter break, the Snowflake family travels to the beautiful beaches of Florida to escape the cold weather. Frank Snowflake and Sarah Snowflake love the beach, but they miss building their favorite snow sculptures. The Snowflake family decided to bring their snow sculpting materials to the beach this year so they didn't have to miss out on their favorite winter activity. There was only one problem…it took the Snowflake family six hours to move all of the materials from their car, down the sand dunes, and to their favorite spot on the beach. By the time they finished moving the materials to their spot on the beach, there was very little time to build a sand sculpture.

Can you help the Snowflake family by building a sled that will travel down a ramp and help them move all of their materials in one trip?

MISSION

Build a sled that can move a load down a ramp in the fastest amount of time without dropping anything.

BLUEPRINT EXPLORE

Provide the Individual Blueprint Design sheet, and ask students to sketch a design for a prototype they will describe to the other members of their team. After each team member has presented his or her design, the team as a whole will decide which prototype to construct and then draw it on the Group Blueprint Design sheet. Next, the team will present the design to the teacher for approval and for permission to retrieve their materials and begin construction.

ENGINEERING TASK   TEST TRIAL   ANALYZE   REDESIGN

ENGINEERING TASK

Each team will build a sled that will move materials.

TEST TRIAL

Each team will test its sled in the testing box the teacher prepared ahead of time. The team must choose the height of its ramp (3 inches, 5 inches, or 7 inches measured from the tallest point).

The team will release its sled from the top of the ramp. The teacher will use a stopwatch to record the time it takes the sled to travel down the ramp and come to a stop.

Note: The different ramp heights represent different sand dunes the Snowflake family can choose to move their materials down.

ANALYZE

Teams will determine the success of their design based on whether or not the materials remained on the sled. Teams will also observe the time it takes for their sled to reach the sandy beach.

Teams should be allowed to observe the other designs to gather ideas, reflect, and make changes in order to improve their prototypes.

REDESIGN

Teams can use a colored pencil to make adjustments to their original design sketches. Teams will present the changes to the teacher for approval before making changes to the prototypes. Then they can get new supplies to rebuild and retest their prototypes.

HELPFUL TIPS

- After the Test Trial, have teams take a gallery walk to view other teams' designs for possible ideas to assist them in the Analyze and Redesign portions of the engineering design process.

- If teams are successful on the first try, encourage them to make their prototypes even more efficient. If it is a scenario in which this is not feasible, distribute team members to other teams to be a support for them in making their prototypes more efficient. Alternatively, at teacher discretion, move students on to the Justification portion of the lesson.

- If after the third test the final prototype is still unsuccessful, ask students how they would start over. These challenges are meant to have students build on what they originally designed. If the design proved to be unsuccessful, encourage a reflection/justification on what they would do if they were allowed to start again from scratch.

REFLECTIONS — EXPLAIN & ELABORATE

AFTER TEST TRIAL 1	Did the load stay on your sled? How long did it take for your sled to move down the ramp? How does your sled compare to other teams' sleds?
ANALYSIS	What changes will you make to your prototype? Will you use the same ramp height? Explain.
AFTER TEST TRIAL 2	Did the load stay on your sled? How long did it take for your sled to move down the ramp? How does your sled compare to the other teams' sleds?
ANALYSIS	What changes will you make to your prototype? Will you use the same ramp height? Explain.
AFTER TEST TRIAL 3	What team had the fastest sled? How did this sled compare to the other teams' sleds? Did the load stay on your sled?

JUSTIFICATION — EVALUATE

ARTS	Use art materials to make the Snowflake family.
ELA	Draw, tell, or write a story about the Snowflake family's day at the beach. Include details about how they used your sled.

THAT'S SHADY!

2-3 HOURS

TIME FOR COMPLETION

SETTING —THE— **STAGE**

DESIGN CHALLENGE PURPOSE

Build a shelter to provide shade for a playground.

TEACHER DEVELOPMENT

Radiation is the process of giving off energy in the form of waves or particles. The **sun** is the closest star to the earth and gives off radiation. This radiation can be absorbed by all living and nonliving things, especially objects that are made of metal. Most playgrounds have metal parts. Even plastic and wood can absorb enough heat to cause burns to the skin.

STUDENT DEVELOPMENT

Students will need to have background knowledge of how to read temperatures and understand that it is best to play outside in lower **temperatures** or underneath shade. Students will need to understand that **shade** can reduce the temperature of the area it covers.

Students need to have an understanding of how energy from the sun can cause objects made of metal and plastic to heat up.

Lesson Idea: Discuss with students why they should not touch a stove when it is on. This can lead into how other things that are hot are also dangerous to touch. Take students to the playground on a sunny day, and have them stand in full sun for a few minutes. Allow them to describe what they feel. Repeat this procedure in the shade. This will provide them with a better understanding of how thermal energy warms things and why a shade will allow them to safely use the playground on sunny days.

STANDARDS

SCIENCE	TECHNOLOGY	ENGINEERING	ARTS	MATH	ELA
K-PS3-2		K-2-ETS1-1	Creating #1	CCSS.MATH. CONTENT.K.MD.A.2	CCSS.ELA-LITERACY.SL.K.3
		K-2-ETS1-2	Creating #2		
		K-2-ETS1-3	Creating #3		

SCIENCE & ENGINEERING PRACTICES

Constructing Explanations and Designing Solutions: Use tools and/or materials to design and/or build a device that solves a specific problem or a solution to a specific problem.

CROSSCUTTING CONCEPTS

Cause and Effect: Events have causes that generate observable patterns.

TARGET VOCABULARY

canopy

heat

shade

sunlight

temperature

tent

MATERIALS

- clay
- construction paper (light and dark colors)
- fabric (light and dark colors)
- thermometers
- wooden skewers
- craft sticks
- tape
- scissors
- temperature data sheet (page 143)

LITERACY CONNECTIONS

Manners on the Playground by Carrie Finn

Sun Up, Sun Down by Gail Gibbons

NOTES

DILEMMA — ENGAGE

The principal of Blazing Elementary School has a problem. He noticed that the students do not want to play on the playground equipment during very sunny days because it is too hot to touch. He decided to ask teams to design a cover to protect the students and equipment on hot sunny days. Can your team build a shade structure for the playground equipment?

MISSION

Build a prototype for a cover to protect the playground equipment from the heat of the sun.

BLUEPRINT — EXPLORE

Provide the Individual Blueprint Design sheet, and ask students to sketch a design for a prototype they will describe to the other members of their team. After each team member has presented his or her design, the team as a whole will decide which prototype to construct and then draw it on the Group Blueprint Design sheet. Next, the team will present the design to the teacher for approval and for permission to retrieve their materials and begin construction.

ENGINEERING TASK   TEST TRIAL   ANALYZE   REDESIGN

ENGINEERING TASK

Each team will build a prototype for a protective shelter for a playground.

TEST TRIAL

Each team will use a thermometer to record the temperature in direct sunlight and under the shade of the prototype after 2 minutes and again after 10 minutes. Team members should compare the temperature recordings.

Note: The teacher should help teams read the temperature on their thermometers.

ANALYZE

Teams will determine whether or not their shade prototypes helped reduce the temperature underneath. They will then compare their temperature readings to the temperatures recorded by other teams.

Teams should be allowed to observe the other designs to gather ideas, reflect, and make changes in order to improve their prototypes.

Note: Teams should notice that the prototypes made with light colored materials will have lower temperatures than prototypes made with darker colored materials.

REDESIGN

Teams can use a colored pencil to make adjustments to their original design sketches. Teams will present the changes to the teacher for approval before making changes to the prototypes. Then they can get new supplies to rebuild and retest their prototypes.

HELPFUL TIPS

- After the Test Trial, have teams take a gallery walk to view other teams' designs for possible ideas to assist them in the Analyze and Redesign portions of the engineering design process.

- If teams are successful on the first try, encourage them to make their prototypes even more efficient. If it is a scenario in which this is not feasible, distribute team members to other teams to be a support for them in making their prototypes more efficient. Alternatively, at teacher discretion, move students on to the Justification portion of the lesson.

- If after the third test the final prototype is still unsuccessful, ask students how they would start over. These challenges are meant to have students build on what they originally designed. If the design proved to be unsuccessful, encourage a reflection/justification on what they would do if they were allowed to start again from scratch.

     STEAM Design Challenges Gr. K © 2017 Creative Teaching Press

REFLECTIONS | EXPLAIN & ELABORATE

AFTER TEST TRIAL 1	Was the temperature under your prototype higher or lower than the temperature in direct sunlight?
ANALYSIS	Which team had the lowest temperature? Why do you think its prototype had the lowest temperature?
AFTER TEST TRIAL 2	Did the second test of your prototype have a lower temperature than your first test?
ANALYSIS	How can you improve your design?
AFTER TEST TRIAL 3	Did your team's prototype lower the temperature of the area directly under it?

JUSTIFICATION | EVALUATE

ARTS	Create a unique design to decorate your shade covering using your school colors or mascot.

APPENDIX

BEAR GETS READY TO HIBERNATE

By _____

GLUE

NO TRESPASSING!

Today's date is _____.

Today's cloud cover is:

sunny   partly cloudy   cloudy

Today's wind is:

calm   windy   very windy

Today's precipitation is:

none   rain   snow   other

Today's temperature is _____.

hot   90°   warm   75°   cool   65°   cold   40°

How should someone dress today?

How many days was it:

sunny?

partly cloudy?

cloudy?

calm?

windy?

very windy?

How many days was there:

no precipitation?

rain?

snow?

other?

How many days was it:

hot?

warm?

cool?

cold?

How many days should someone have worn:

(title)

TEST TRIAL 1	TEST TRIAL 2	TEST TRIAL 3

This habitat is called

_____

It has _____ trees.

It has _____ plants.

It has _____ water sources.

It has _____ food sources.

Directions: Color the days you plan to water your plant.

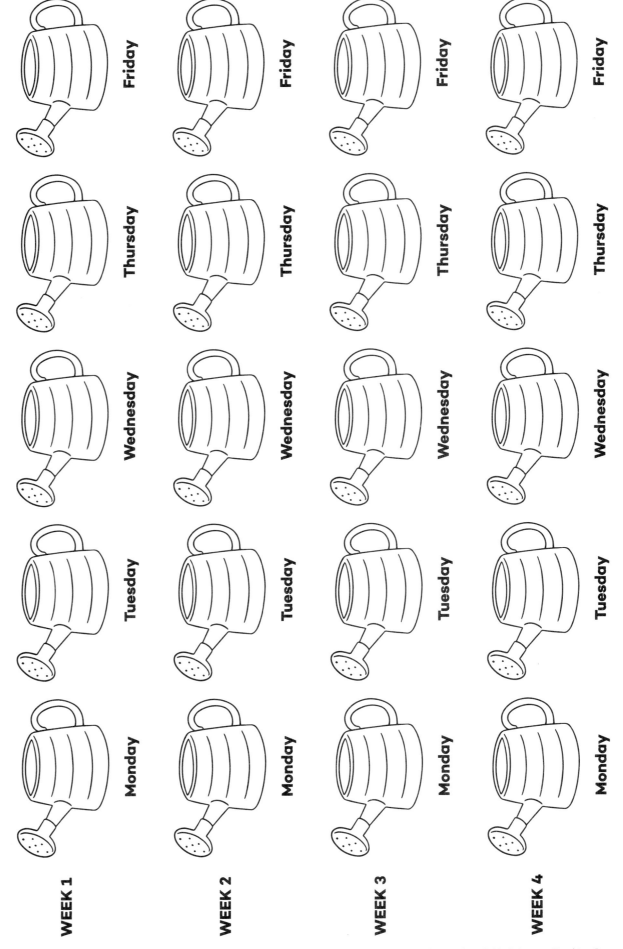

WEEK 1   Monday   Tuesday   Wednesday   Thursday   Friday

WEEK 2   Monday   Tuesday   Wednesday   Thursday   Friday

WEEK 3   Monday   Tuesday   Wednesday   Thursday   Friday

WEEK 4   Monday   Tuesday   Wednesday   Thursday   Friday

Draw a map of your classroom. Include your teacher's desk, the doors, and the windows. Draw an X in the best spot for growing your plant.

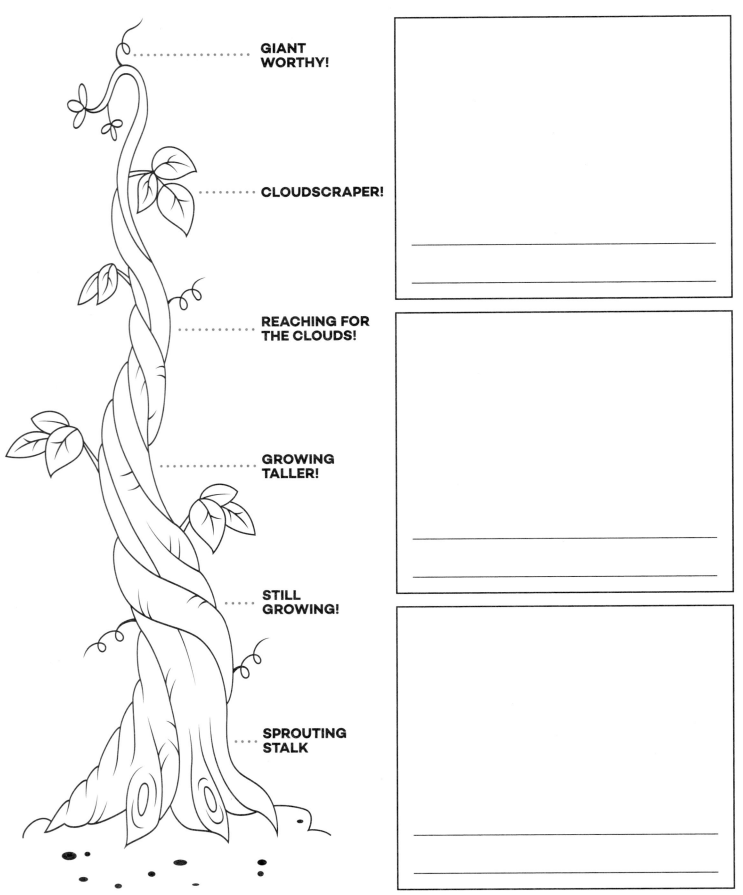

GIANT
WORTHY!

CLOUDSCRAPER!

REACHING FOR
THE CLOUDS!

GROWING
TALLER!

STILL
GROWING!

SPROUTING
STALK

cow

grass

farm

squirrel

nuts

oak tree

salmon

small insects

river

sparrow

seeds

trees

turtle

snails

pond

alligator

fish

swamp

Certificate of

APPRECIATION

This certifies that

_____

helped the Natural History Museum repair its animal displays.

Dr. Docent

Dr. Docent

GOLDILOCKS AND THE THREE BEARS

By

_____

GLUE

Thanks for your help!

EGG-STREME 500

CUP SERIES

Your friend, Humpty Dumpty

142

THAT'S SHADY!–TEMPERATURE DATA SHEET

	After 2 minutes:	After 10 minutes:
temperature in the sunlight		
temperature in the shade after Test Trial 1		
temperature in the shade after Test Trial 2		
temperature in the shade after Test Trial 3		

✂ -

	After 2 minutes:	After 10 minutes:
temperature in the sunlight		
temperature in the shade after Test Trial 1		
temperature in the shade after Test Trial 2		
temperature in the shade after Test Trial 3		

Draw!	
Share!	
Listen!	
Choose!	

TEACHER APPROVAL:

 VOCABULARY

VOCABULARY WORD	DEFINITION	DRAW THE MEANING

 WHAT I LEARNED

Construction Specialist

Description: This person is the one whose design was chosen. This person builds the prototype and is responsible for ensuring that the prototype follows the design rules exactly.

Material Resource Officer

Description: This person is in charge of getting, measuring, and cutting materials for the prototypes. This person assists the construction specialist by getting materials ready and assisting in construction.

Engineering Supervisor

Description: This person is the team leader. This person assists all other team members as needed. This person acts as spokesperson for the team. This person will test the team's prototype.

Cheerleader

Description: This person helps and encourages team members and cheers on success and effort.

STEAM Design Challenges Gr. K © 2017 Creative Teaching Press

My Inventor's Notebook

_____
Name

STEAM DESIGN CHALLENGES TEAM RUBRIC

	EXEMPLARY	PROFICIENT	PROGRESSING	BEGINNING
DESIGN	Team members reach consensus as to which prototype to construct. They complete team blueprint design sheet in which they include their reasons for selecting the team prototype. They include a written or verbal explanation to compare and contrast the prototypes they sketched individually. Prototype is constructed according to specifications in the team blueprint design.	Team members reach consensus as to which prototype to construct. They include their reasons for selecting the prototype but do not include a written or verbal explanation to compare and contrast the prototypes they sketched individually. Prototype is constructed according to the specifications in the team blueprint design.	Team members reach consensus as to which prototype to construct. They include their reasons for selecting the prototype but do not include a written or verbal explanation to compare and contrast the prototypes they sketched individually. Prototype is not constructed according to the specifications of the blueprint design.	Team members reach consensus as to which prototype to construct. They do not include either their reasons for selecting the prototype or a written or verbal explanation to compare and contrast the prototypes they sketched. Prototype is constructed.
TEST	Teams test their prototypes. Teams record or verbalize their observations that align with the design challenge. They make note of any unique design flaws.	Teams test their prototypes and record or verbalize their observations that align with the design challenge.	Teams test their prototypes. They record or verbalize observations that do not align with the design challenge.	Teams test their prototypes. They do not record observations.

STEAM DESIGN CHALLENGES TEAM RUBRIC

	EXEMPLARY	PROFICIENT	PROGRESSING	BEGINNING
ANALYZE	Team members participate in an analytic discussion about their testing and observations. They reflect on their design as compared to at least three other teams. They discuss their intended redesign steps, defending their reasoning in their discussion.	Team members participate in an analytic discussion about their testing and observations. They reflect on their design as compared to at least two other teams. They discuss their intended redesign steps.	Team members participate in an analytic discussion about their testing and observations, comparing their design with at least one other team's. They discuss their intended redesign steps.	Team members participate in an analytic discussion about their testing but do not compare their design with another team's. They discuss their intended redesign steps.
REDESIGN	Team redesigns its prototype. Original sketch is altered using a colored pencil to illustrate changes made with supporting reasons.	Team redesigns its prototype. Original sketch is altered using a colored pencil to illustrate changes made.	Team redesigns its prototype. Original sketch is altered to illustrate changes made.	Team redesigns its prototype.
EVALUATE	Team completes a justification activity. Team reflects and makes meaningful connections to the science standards as well as to two of the other STEAM standards addressed in the lesson.	Team completes a justification activity. Team reflects and makes meaningful connections to the science standards as well as to one of the other STEAM standards addressed in the lesson.	Team completes a justification activity. Team reflects and makes meaningful connections to the science standards addressed in the lesson.	Team completes a justification activity. Team makes no connection to the science standards addressed in the lesson.

BIBLIOGRAPHY

"5 Steps to Growing Lima Beans Indoors." DoItYourself. Accessed October 10, 2016.
http://www.doityourself.com/stry/3-steps-to-growing-lima-beans-indoors.

"Animal Habitats for Kids." Skyenimals. Accessed September 28, 2016.
http://www.skyenimals.com/browse_habitat.cgi.

"Buoyancy." Sandbox Networks. Accessed September 29, 2016.
https://www.teachervision.com/math/resource/5987.html.

"Create a Storybook." My Storybook. Accessed October 9, 2016. https://www.mystorybook.com/.

Dunn, Becca. "Playground Equipment Can Cause Burns Even on Mild Days." Newsy. Accessed
September 21, 2016.
http://www.newsy.com/videos/playground-equipment-can-cause-burns-even-on-mild-days/.

Gross, Rebecca. "Stilt Houses: 10 Reasons to Get Your House Off the Ground." Houzz. Accessed
October 6, 2016.
http://www.houzz.com/ideabooks/35270725/list/stilt-houses-10-reasons-to-get-your-house-off-the-ground.

"How to Prepare Your Home for a Natural Disaster." BlackMoldRemoval.com. Accessed October 9, 2016.
https://www.blackmoldremoval.com/natural-disaster-preparation/.

Karre, Nancy, and Paul Drummond. "Introduction." *Teacher's Guide: Kindergarten Unit Forces and
Interaction*. Accessed September 23, 2016.
http://www.mccracken.kyschools.us/Downloads/PUSHES%20and%20PULLS%20-K.pdf

Oden, Dirk. "Sir Isaac and Seat Belts." Science Perspectives. Accessed August 22, 2016.
http://www.scienceperspectives.com/Sir-Isaac-and-Seat-Belts.htm.

"Weather." NOAA Education. Accessed September 15, 2016.
http://www.education.noaa.gov/tweather.html.

"When Play Equipment Is Too Hot to Handle." CBS News. Accessed September 21, 2016.
http://www.cbsnews.com/news/when-play-equipment-is-too-hot-to-handle/.